The
Spelling Practice Workbook
6th Grade

Also by Natasha Attard, Ph.D.

Vocabulary Building 7th Grade Workbook: Guided Activities to
Increase your Word Power. Consolidates and Complements
Homeschooling of the English Language

Vocabulary and Spelling Practice Grade 7: Intensive Practice
Workbook and Guided Activities to Increase Your Word Power.

The Spelling Practice Workbook Grade 7: Guided Activities to
Increase your Word Power. Consolidates and Complements
Homeschooling of the English Language

The Spelling Practice Workbook 8th Grade with Vocabulary Definitions,
Model Sentences and Final Assessments: Guided Spelling Activities for 8th Grade.

The SPELLING PRACTICE Workbook

6th Grade

Vocabulary Definitions
Model Sentences
Final Assessments

Guided Spelling Activities for the 6th Grade

Natasha Attard Ph.D

First published 2023

ISBN 978-9918-0-0671-7 Paperback

To my boys, Giovanni and Beppe, with much love.

Contents

About this Book

This workbook is designed to assist 6th grade students in developing strong spelling skills while concurrently enhancing their word comprehension and usage. While the primary emphasis of this workbook is on spelling accuracy, it also aims to improve students' long-term word retention through simultaneous practice of spelling drills and application of vocabulary in context. The structure of each lesson in this workbook is tailored to facilitate this dual learning process.

This workbook consists of 20 lessons, with each lesson centered around five words. Each spelling activity is tailored to these words and includes their definitions and example sentences, aiding students in understanding word meanings as they practice spelling. In total, 6th grade students are expected to learn a vocabulary of 100 words.

Each lesson begins with a syllable-based drilling activity, allowing students to systematically practice the correct spelling of each word component. Following the syllable drill, students proceed to another drilling exercise using the complete word to further reinforce their spelling practice.

To enhance both spelling accuracy and word comprehension, each lesson incorporates a word search puzzle featuring the target words and their synonyms. This engaging activity helps students remain attentive to word meanings. Additionally, every lesson concludes with a sentence composition exercise, enabling students to construct sentences that incorporate the target words.

Students can track their progress using the dedicated notes pages provided throughout this workbook. Furthermore, ten multiple-choice spelling tests are included at the end of the workbook, allowing them to assess their spelling proficiency.

The Spelling Practice Workbook for 6th Grade offers a comprehensive and engaging approach to improving spelling skills. It provides 6th grade students with the opportunity to practice both accurate spelling and word usage within meaningful contexts.

How to Use this Book

Teachers and parents can use this workbook as a supplement to their regular spelling instruction or as a standalone resource. The structured approach, featuring 20 lessons with four practice exercises per lesson, facilitates seamless integration into any teaching or learning environment.

To begin each lesson, students should start by reviewing the word bank consisting of five words and their respective definitions and model sentences. Next, they should proceed to complete the syllable-based drilling exercise for each word. Learning to spell words in syllables is a valuable skill that enhances accuracy, promotes knowledge retention, and builds phonetic awareness. Afterward, students should move on to the next drilling exercise, this time focusing on the entire word. Following the completion of the drilling exercises, students should engage in the word search puzzle that incorporates the five target words along with their synonyms. This is followed by a synonym pairing activity. This activity not only reinforces learning but also makes it enjoyable and engaging. To conclude the lesson, students should undertake the final activity of composing sentences using the target words. This exercise serves to consolidate their spelling practice and reinforce their understanding of word usage.

At the end of this workbook, there are ten multiple-choice spelling tests that students should complete after finishing the 20 lessons. These tests are designed to assess the progress made and identify areas that may need further revision.

To facilitate the needs of teachers and parents who wish to concentrate on a particular lesson, the table of contents in this workbook provides a list of the word banks included in each lesson. This list can also serve as a reference for other language activities and testing purposes.

A Message from the Author

Dear Reader,

Thank you for choosing "The Spelling Practice Workbook for 6th Grade." As an educator and author, my deepest passion lies in guiding students through the intricacies of language. I am dedicated to helping each young learner overcome the hurdles they face in writing, particularly in spelling and vocabulary usage. It is my earnest belief that every student has the potential to excel in these areas, and it's my mission to unlock this potential through resources that are both educational and engaging.

To further support your child's academic journey, I'm excited to offer an exclusive, complimentary resource from my other publication, "Vocabulary and Spelling Practice for 7th Grade." This free online resource, accessible with your purchase, includes the first three lessons from "Vocabulary and Spelling Practice for 7th Grade." It's designed to align with the skills and knowledge your child is developing through "The Spelling Practice Workbook for 6th Grade."

What's Inside This Free Resource?
- **Guided Exercises**: Engaging activities that introduce vocabulary words, emphasizing their connotations and meanings in a way that's understandable and relatable for 7th graders.
- **Comprehensive Definitions:** Each word is accompanied by clear definitions and multiple example sentences, enhancing understanding through context.
- **Practical Application:** Diverse exercises for repeated practice, alongside spelling lessons that incorporate fun games. This approach ensures a deeper grasp of vocabulary and spelling.
- **Self-Assessment Tools:** At the end of the lesson, your child can test their knowledge, helping you track their progress and identify areas for improvement.

How to Access:
Scan the Code and it will take you to my website (natashascripts.com). Enter your name and email address and you will be redirected instantly to the free resource.

Warm regards,

Natasha Attard Ph.d

Lesson 1

Definitions

Adjacent: two things that are right next to each other, e.g. two buildings.

Blown: (i) past participle of 'blow' referring to something that has been moved or carried.
(ii) destroyed or damaged.

Catastrophe: a big and terrible event such as an earthquake or other disaster.

Disastrous: something that has gone really wrong, producing a huge mess.

Equator: an invisible line that goes around the middle of the earth, dividing it into the northern and southern hemisphere.

Example Sentences

My best friend's house is next to mine, so we are lucky to be neighbors because we have fun playing together in our **adjacent** yards.

(i) The leaves were **blown** away by the strong wind.
(ii) The building was **blown** to pieces during the bombing.

Last year's hurricane was a **catastrophe** for our town because lots of homes and buildings were damaged, making a mess everywhere.

Our science experiment mixing vinegar with baking soda turned out to be **disastrous** because it overflowed all over the lab bench.

During our geography class we learned that countries near the **equator** tend to have warm climates.

Practice *the* Tricky letters

Let's Practice Spelling the Word

Keep Going!

d **j** adjacent	ad - ja - cent ⟶	
ow blown	blown ⟶	
tas **phe** catastrophe	ca - tas - tro - phe ⟶	
as **ous** disastrous	dis - as - trous ⟶	
eq **ua** **or** equator	e - qua - tor ⟶	

Now write each word in full.

adjacent		⟶
blown		⟶
catastrophe		⟶
disastrous		⟶
equator		⟶

Practice makes Perfect!

Synonyms Puzzle 1

```
            S  V  D  F
         O  K  I  U  Y  A  D  D
      D  E  F  N  V  C  O  E  T  E  L  E
   F  V  A  C  I  A  F  V  R  M  A  W  J  U
   O  M  G  D  R  G  A  S  G  T  G  Z  A  A
   B  A  Q  H  R  J  S  A  O  Y  N  S  I  I  C  Q
   J  Q  V  I  X  T  A  E  C  I  Z  N  A  A  X  T
V  X  W  E  M  A  O  J  C  R  N  Q  T  T  S  S  W  H
L  N  D  H  T  N  W  J  O  E  L  H  A  A  P  I  S  Z
U  X  W  I  T  X  E  B  C  X  N  S  O  H  B  R  D  Q
S  L  N  O  E  U  H  N  D  C  T  T  R  F  F  O  E  R
D  G  D  O  L  G  H  Q  H  R  V  E  Q  E  L  T  P  S
   E  F  E  I  B  U  E  O  Z  T  L  H  J  N  A  O
   F  O  E  D  V  Q  P  S  S  P  M  I  P  O  U  J
      N  R  B  O  H  M  A  X  D  Z  X  M  T  Q
      V  A  W  E  L  S  X  J  Z  O  D  T  V  E
         S  Z  F  I  P  L  J  I  U  D  T  A
            D  O  K  X  L  K  G  U
               L  C  E  F
```

ADJACENT	BLOWN	CARRIED
CATASTROPHE	DEVASTATING	DISASTER
DISASTROUS	EQUATOR	EXPLODED
NEIGHBORING		

Synonyms

adjacent	——————→	
blown	——————→	
catastrophe	——————→	
disastrous	——————→	
equator	——————→	no synonym

Let's Compose Sentences

Look back at the definitions and example sentences. Can you write a sentence for each of the words?

Adjacent: _____

_____

Blown: _____

_____

Catastrophe: _____

_____

Disastrous: _____

_____

Equator: _____

_____

My Notes

Use this page for:
i. dictionary work
ii. challenging spelling
iii. challenging definitions
iv. new synonyms learned
v. further practice

Lesson 2

Definitions

Acquire: to get or obtain something.

Belief: something you think is true or have faith in.

Connection: a link or relationship between things or people.

Dazzling: describes something that is very bright, impressive or amazing.

Exaggerate: to make something seem bigger or worse than it is.

Example Sentences

They were amazed at how quickly she **acquired** her riding skills without using training wheels.

Learning about different cultures and their **beliefs** can be a fascinating way to understand the world better.

The detective finally made the **connection** between the note found at the crime scene and the suspect in the case.

The fireworks display on the Fourth of July was absolutely **dazzling**, with bursts of colorful lights filling the night sky.

When he tells a story, he tends to **exaggerate**, to make his tale more exciting.

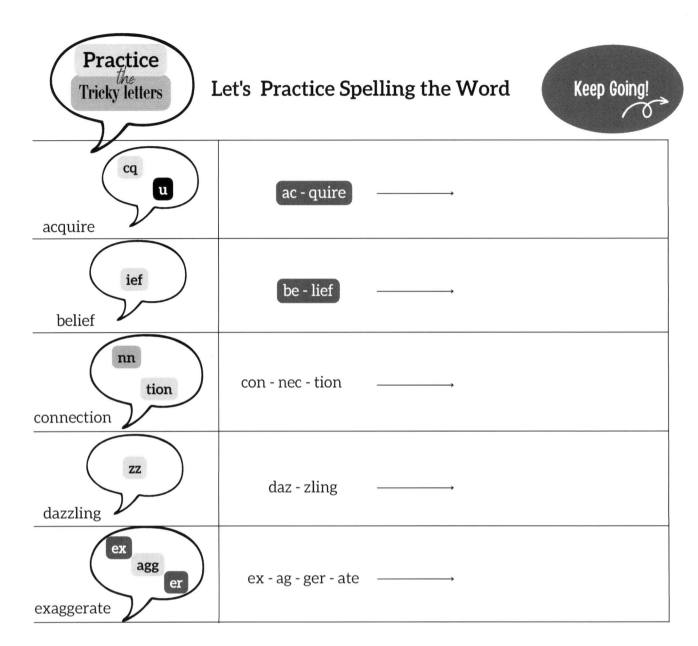

cq **u** acquire	ac - quire ⟶
ief belief	be - lief ⟶
nn tion connection	con - nec - tion ⟶
zz dazzling	daz - zling ⟶
ex agg **er** exaggerate	ex - ag - ger - ate ⟶

Now write each word in full.

acquire	⟶
belief	⟶
connection	⟶
dazzling	⟶
exaggerate	⟶

Practice
makes
Perfect!

	→	
	→	
	→	
	→	
	→	

	→	
	→	
	→	
	→	
	→	

Synonyms Puzzle 2

```
V  U  A  E  T  P  D  H  T  R  B  A  B  W  Z  H  K  P  X  O
A  L  M  L  X  F  B  M  A  G  N  I  F  Y  A  M  V  A  B  S
L  I  N  K  W  Z  H  X  E  I  U  G  Y  C  J  R  P  T  S  M
Z  W  S  N  V  K  S  C  B  W  V  G  Q  V  A  H  A  C  H  J
K  V  S  C  T  R  K  I  W  S  S  U  G  R  S  I  U  U  X  Y
I  A  O  D  F  G  H  I  D  O  I  X  A  I  N  P  W  O  A  B
N  U  T  J  A  T  Z  T  T  R  P  D  J  L  S  W  S  Q  F  B
U  D  G  H  X  E  G  P  E  K  I  D  K  P  R  L  M  P  G  E
R  Y  N  E  E  N  S  X  E  A  D  K  Z  L  Y  K  R  V  X  S
Z  G  Q  T  B  K  V  W  N  J  R  W  N  L  M  S  Y  A  W  H
J  M  G  P  J  C  G  T  S  A  N  C  M  S  Z  P  G  K  Y  N
Q  W  B  L  S  N  T  J  V  O  U  R  C  F  M  G  D  S  M  O
J  B  Z  M  P  H  L  M  I  E  T  Y  A  M  E  C  L  W  H  I
U  Q  T  R  C  F  M  T  S  H  A  P  W  R  Z  D  Q  Y  X  T
G  I  Y  C  S  R  C  O  F  U  B  Q  A  U  I  F  Q  L  E  C
Y  N  H  Y  L  E  V  E  I  T  Z  D  A  L  F  W  K  L  I
Y  F  I  I  N  M  I  K  O  Y  E  S  B  J  V  L  I  R  L  V
U  M  Q  N  G  L  Q  F  D  H  F  G  D  O  X  I  P  P  Y  N
I  W  O  C  E  O  A  D  A  Z  Z  L  I  N  G  H  O  T  A  O
S  C  O  B  R  U  D  I  W  P  T  U  Z  O  B  R  P  W  W  C
```

ACQUIRE	BELIEF	CONNECTION
CONVICTION	DAZZLING	EXAGGERATE
LINK	MAGNIFY	OBTAIN
RADIANT		

Synonyms

acquire	——————→	
belief	——————→	
connection	——————→	
dazzling	——————→	
exaggerate	——————→	

Let's Compose Sentences

Look back at the definitions and example sentences. Can you write a sentence for each of the words?

Aquire: _____

_____

Belief: _____

_____

Connection: _____

_____

Dazzling: _____

_____

Exaggerate: _____

_____

My Notes

Lesson 3

Definitions

Ancient: something which is extremely old, having existed for a long time in the past.

Bough: a big branch of a tree, especially one that comes off the main trunk of the tree.

Comfortable: feeling relaxed and at ease.

Departure: the act of leaving or going away.

Encouragement: words or actions that give support to help someone do their best or keep going.

Example Sentences

The pyramids of Giza are considered to be **ancient** because they were built thousands of years ago.

The squirrel leaped from **bough** to **bough**, searching for nuts in the tree.

The new mattress made her bed much more **comfortable**, and she slept soundly through the night.

The **departure** of the train was delayed by an hour due to a heavy snowfall.

His friends offered words of **encouragement** before he stepped onto the stage to give his speech.

Let's Practice Spelling the Word

Keep Going!

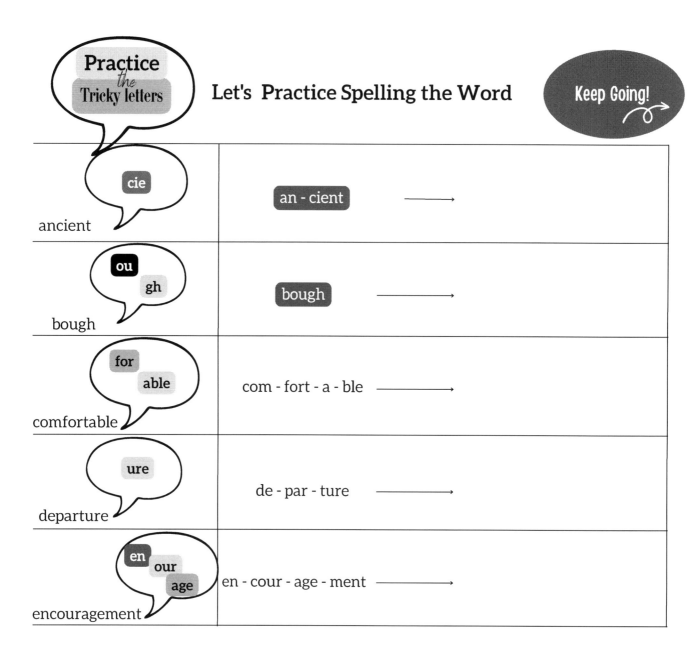

cie ancient	an - cient ⟶
ou **gh** bough	bough ⟶
for **able** comfortable	com - fort - a - ble ⟶
ure departure	de - par - ture ⟶
en **our** **age** encouragement	en - cour - age - ment ⟶

Now write each word in full.

ancient		⟶
bough		⟶
comfortable		⟶
departure		⟶
encouragement		⟶

Practice
makes
Perfect!

	→	
	→	
	→	
	→	
	→	

	→	
	→	
	→	
	→	
	→	

Synonyms Puzzle 3

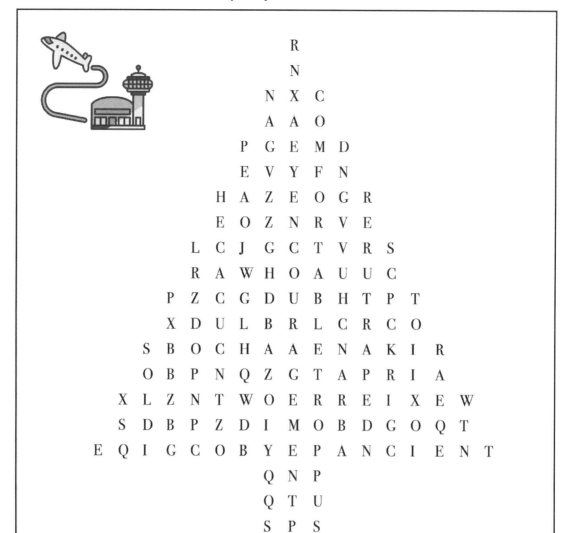

```
                              R
                              N
                        N  X  C
                        A  A  O
                     P  G  E  M  D
                     E  V  Y  F  N
                  H  A  Z  E  O  G  R
                  E  O  Z  N  R  V  E
               L  C  J  G  C  T  V  R  S
               R  A  W  H  O  A  U  U  C
            P  Z  C  G  D  U  B  H  T  P  T
            X  D  U  L  B  R  L  C  R  C  O
         S  B  O  C  H  A  A  E  N  A  K  I  R
         O  B  P  N  Q  Z  G  T  A  P  R  I  A
      X  L  Z  N  T  W  O  E  R  R  E  I  X  E  W
      S  D  B  P  Z  D  I  M  O  B  D  G  O  Q  T
   E  Q  I  G  C  O  B  Y  E  P  A  N  C  I  E  N  T
                        Q  N  P
                        Q  T  U
                        S  P  S
```

ANCIENT	BOUGH	BRANCH
COMFORTABLE	COZY	DEPARTURE
ENCOURAGEMENT	LEAVE	OLD
SUPPORT		

Synonyms

ancient	⟶	
bough	⟶	
comfortable	⟶	
departure	⟶	
encouragement	⟶	

Let's Compose Sentences

Look back at the definitions and example sentences. Can you write a sentence for each of the words?

Ancient: _____

_____

Bough: _____

_____

Comfortable: _____

_____

Departure: _____

_____

Encouragement: _____

_____

My Notes

Lesson 4

Definitions

Focus: to pay close attention and work on something with a clear goal.

Government: the organization that makes laws, manages public affairs and provides services to a country or state.

Harmonious: existing in a peaceful and friendly way without conflicts.

Irrigate: to supply water to land by using pipes to help plants grow.

Junior: describes someone that is younger or lower in rank or grade.

Example Sentences

She could not **focus** on her book because of all the noise in the room.

The **government** is responsible for making and enforcing laws that help keep the country safe.

She loved spending time at her grandparents' house because it was surrounded by trees and had a **harmonious** atmosphere.

The ancient civilizations of Mesopotamia were known for their creative methods to **irrigate** their farmlands.

My older brother is a **junior** in high school, so he'll graduate next year.

c us focus	fo - cus ⟶
go er government	gov - ern - ment ⟶
i harmonious	har - mo - ni - ous ⟶
rr irrigate	ir - ri - gate ⟶
j io junior	jun - ior ⟶

Now write each word in full.

focus		⟶
government		⟶
harmonious		⟶
irrigate		⟶
junior		⟶

Practice
makes
Perfect!

Synonyms Puzzle 4

```
        I  B  X  Y  D  Q              K  W  J  B  V  O
     A  A  R  K  Q  Q  O  Y           A  N  L  D  R  Y  G  C
     H  D  S  R  Q  F  Q  U  V     W  L  W  O  Z  H  K  O  A
     R  H  M  O  I  Q  F  H  P  T  Z  U  Z  G  Z  M  E  N  B  Y
     O  W  H  I  G  G  O  V  E  R  N  M  E  N  T  C  I  W  Y
     I  E  Y  P  N  M  A  G  W  V  H  G  L  G  E  K  T  K  E
     N  V  Q  P  V  I  S  T  H  W  S  J  P  W  N  R  V  B  P  K
     U  K  C  X  G  J  S  P  E  P  S  H  N  T  X  Z  M  V  G  I
     J  B  Y  N  B  L  W  T  Q  M  O  T  R  D  V  L  S  M  S  C
     D  U  G  W  R  U  F  G  R  R  H  A  K  N  Y  U  L  U  V  F
     S  Z  H  K  J  F  V  L  Y  A  T  S  Z  I  W  B  O  K  O  W
        E  G  Q  E  E  X  E  T  E  T  G  Q  V  X  I  I  C  A
           H  Z  G  C  D  V  R  A  Q  I  F  J  N  L  U  T
              Y  N  A  E  S  E  L  E  J  O  O  H  S  E
                 M  E  K  T  G  W  H  G  M  N  L  R
                    P  P  P  N  Q  H  R  W  Y  V
                       J  Z  U  Q  A  I  J  S
                          D  O  H  B  U  Z
                             Y  Y  C  V
                                I  N
```

ADMINISTRATION	CONCENTRATE	FOCUS
GOVERNMENT	HARMONIOUS	IRRIGATE
JUNIOR	PEACEFUL	WATER
YOUNGER		

Synonyms

focus	⟶
government	⟶
harmonious	⟶
irrigate	⟶
junior	⟶

Let's Compose Sentences

Look back at the definitions and example sentences. Can you write a sentence for each of the words?

Focus: _____

_____

Government: _____

_____

Harmonious: _____

_____

Irrigate: _____

_____

Junior: _____

_____

My Notes

Lesson 5

Definitions

Fragile: delicate and needing careful handling.

Gaze: to look steadily and intently at something or someone.

Involve: to participate in a particular activity, event or situation.

Jovial: cheerful and friendly.

Knowledge: what a person knows such as facts and information.

Example Sentences

The **fragile** butterfly's wings were a beautiful shade of blue.

She **gazed** at the night sky filled with twinkling stars.

The Christmas school pageant **involved** students from 6th and 7th grade singing carols, acting out holiday scenes, and spreading festive cheer to the audience.

The classroom was filled with the **jovial** chatter of students as they worked on a fun group project.

Learning from our mistakes is a valuable way to gain **knowledge** and grow as individuals.

Let's Practice Spelling the Word

ile fragile	frag - ile	⟶
z gaze	gaze	⟶
ve involve	in - volve	⟶
j **vi** jovial	jo - vi - al	⟶
k **dg** knowledge	knowl - edge	⟶

Now write each word in full.

fragile		⟶
gaze		⟶
involve		⟶
jovial		⟶
knowledge		⟶

Practice makes Perfect!

⟶	
⟶	
⟶	
⟶	
⟶	

	⟶	
	⟶	
	⟶	
	'	
	⟶	

Synonyms Puzzle 5

```
P                                                         P
E  P                                               W  S
B  X  J                                         V  T  I
Z  J  P  G                                    N  A  V  C
B  R  T  E  Y                              L  R  G  H  L
E  U  B  Y  R  J                        M  E  V  E  R  A
T  F  D  Y  N  T  H                  L  W  U  E  P  L  P
F  I  B  O  Y  J  I  U            R  G  K  R  D  L  K  U
N  R  R  Q  A  F  W  S  C      H  X  H  F  K  A  O  I  B
C  B  A  G  M  I  C  Q  E  K  K  T  S  U  R  T  C  F  U  S
H  M  J  G  F  I  N  C  L  U  D  E  L  I  U  G  G  O  E  V
W  E  M  J  I  I  X  T  P      H  O  O  U  O  U  B  G  K
D  T  L  N  C  L  U  W            M  J  G  N  G  P  D  W
E  A  E  W  H  E                     L  T  K  A  S  E  H
V  C  K  Y  M  A                        U  W  Z  X  L  L
L  I  D  E  B                              V  E  V  W  A
O  L  O  H                                    U  C  O  I
V  E  D                                          Q  N  V
N  D                                                K  O
I                                                      J
```

CHEERFUL	DELICATE	EXPERTISE
FRAGILE	GAZE	INCLUDE
INVOLVE	JOVIAL	KNOWLEDGE
STARE		

Synonyms

fragile	⟶
gaze	⟶
involve	⟶
jovial	⟶
knowledge	⟶

Let's Compose Sentences

Look back at the definitions and example sentences. Can you write a sentence for each of the words?

Fragile: _____

_____

Gaze: _____

_____

Involve: _____

_____

Jovial: _____

_____

Knowledge: _____

_____

My Notes

Lesson 6

Definitions

Labyrinth: like a maze, having paths with twists and turns, making it difficult to find the way out.

Metaphor: a figure of speech that compares two things by saying that one thing is another, e.g. the test was a piece of cake.

Narrate: to tell a story or describe an event in words.

Origin: the place, time or point where something begins.

Peculiar: something strange or unusual that catches attention.

Example Sentences

Tourists visiting the English air raid shelters built during World War 2 always feel like they have entered a **labyrinth** with no clear exit.

The author used a clever **metaphor** to describe the city as a living organism.

She earns a living by **narrating** audiobooks.

They researched the **origin** of their family name, discovering it had roots in Ireland.

She had a **peculiar** habit of always wearing mismatched socks, each with its own unique pattern.

Practice the Tricky letters

Let's Practice Spelling the Word

Keep Going!

y th labyrinth	lab - y - rinth ⟶
ph o metaphor	met - a - phor ⟶
rr narrate	nar - rate ⟶
ri origin	or - i - gin ⟶
cu iar peculiar	pe - cu - liar ⟶

Now write each word in full.

labyrinth		⟶
metaphor		⟶
narrate		⟶
origin		⟶
peculiar		'

	→	
	→	
	→	
	→	
	→	

	→	
	→	
	→	
	→	
	→	

Synonyms Puzzle 6

```
                P  J  F  U
             E  A  J  J  T  Q  Q  F
          D  S  S  K  N  O  I  P  W  F  B  O
       M  A  Z  E  K  R  A  K  B  E  F  G  V  G
       M  W  G  Y  I  U  X  L  C  U  C  E  P  Z
    L  U  M  E  G  M  L  B  L  O  P  N  U  F  G  M
    A  L  R  I  B  E  H        O  G  I  Q  L  N  E
 U  B  M  N  R  W  R           G  Y  G  C  I  T  S
 A  Y  D  D  I  P              C  O  A  N  A  A
 D  R  N  T  X  C              S  D  O  N  P  R
 S  I  L  N  R  N              V  D  Q  I  H  K
 B  N  K  U  A  L  B           M  B  E  Q  G  O  X
    T  W  O  Q  A  V  Y     I  L  J  E  H  E  R
    H  V  C  P  U  K  S  N  I  N  H  T  A  N  B  V
       N  E  U  S  T  X  L  K  A  A  R  J  E  L
       Y  R  R  U  A  F  T  Q  R  M  N  V  U  I
          V  U  N  I  T  C  R  D  N  J  V  B
          U  W  C  A  J  F  D  Z
             N  L  V  L
```

ANALOGY	BEGINNING	LABYRINTH
MAZE	METAPHOR	NARRATE
ORIGIN	PECULIAR	RECOUNT
UNUSUAL		

Synonyms

labyrinth	⟶
metaphor	⟶
narrate	⟶
origin	⟶
peculiar	⟶

Let's Compose Sentences

Look back at the definitions and example sentences. Can you write a sentence for each of the words?

Labyrinth: _____

_____

Metaphor: _____

_____

Narrate: _____

_____

Origin: _____

_____

Peculiar: _____

_____

My Notes

Lesson 7

Definitions

Quote:	to repeat or say exactly what someone else has said or written.
Retrieve:	to get something back, like finding or bringing an item that was lost or misplaced.
Substitute:	a replacement (*noun*), or to replace (*verb*).
Theory:	an idea or explanation based on observations and evidence, used to understand how something works.
Universal:	something that applies to everyone or everything.

Example Sentences

She likes to **quote** famous authors in her essays to make her arguments more convincing.

The dog quickly **retrieved** the ball that had been thrown into the lake.

(i) In many sweet recipes, honey can be used as a **substitute** for sugar.
(ii) In her recipe, she **substituted** sugar with honey.

There are various **theories** about the nature of the universe and its dimensions.

The white dove is a **universal** symbol of peace, recognized by everyone.

q uo — quote	quote ——————→
ie — retrieve	re - trieve ——————→
ute — substitute	sub - sti - tute ——————→
eo — theory	the - ory ——————→
sal — universal	u - ni - ver - sal ——————→

Now write each word in full.

quote		——→
retrieve		——→
substitute		——→
theory		——→
universal		——→

	→	
	→	
	→	
	→	
	→	

	→	
	→	
	→	
	→	
	→	

Synonyms Puzzle 7

```
                    F  C
                 Z  V  D  I
                 J  V  L  B  T
              R  A  J  X  V  K  W  E
           U  E  E  N  Q  C  U  G  J  J
        E  I  P  O  H  C  M  I  O  T  L  C
     G  G  Z  L  D  T  E  K  O  L  A  F  R  I
     Z  I  E  B  A  T  I  S  Q  T  O  P  W  U  B  T
  Q  U  O  T  E  C  M  S  E  U  X  U  G  W  A  E  U  G
U  K  T  D  M  V  E  R  E  T  R  I  E  V  E  D  B  L  K  R
U  N  O  M  D  J  K  I  B  U  F  U  K  B  A  S  O  Y  E  C
  C  I  I  O  T  D  B  T  T  S  M  M  Q  Q  B  R  C  O
     R  V  K  A  V  D  J  I  O  X  H  A  A  O  O  N
        P  E  H  A  C  U  T  O  A  X  L  E  V  C
           T  R  U  T  W  S  C  W  P  H  E  E
              X  S  Y  S  B  N  L  T  R  P
                 A  A  D  U  S  O  K  T
                 Z  L  S  F  U  U
                 B  G  R  F
                 Q  F
```

CITE	CONCEPT	GLOBAL
QUOTE	RECOVER	REPLACE
RETRIEVE	SUBSTITUTE	THEORY
UNIVERSAL		

Synonyms

quote	⟶
retrieve	⟶
substitute	⟶
theory	⟶
universal	⟶

Let's Compose Sentences

Look back at the definitions and example sentences. Can you write a sentence for each of the words?

Quote: _____

_____

Retrieve: _____

_____

Substitute: _____

_____

Theory: _____

_____

Universal: _____

_____

My Notes

Lesson 8

Definitions

Reinforce: to make something stronger by adding support or emphasis.

Source: where something comes from or where you find information about something.

Tangible: something material that you can touch, see or feel because it is real and not abstract or an idea.

Unique: one of a kind that is special and different from the others.

Vivid: clear and detailed, making it easy to remember.

Example Sentences

(i) The steel beams under the bridge **reinforce** its structure, making it very safe.
(ii) Feedback to students helps to **reinforce** learning because it guides them along their educational journey.

(i) Scientists are conducting research to determine the **source** of the unusual seismic activity causing the ongoing ground tremors.
(ii) The internet is a valuable **source** of news and updates from around the world.

The feeling of the soft, warm sand under her feet was a **tangible** pleasure.

Each snow flake that falls is **unique**, and no two have the exact same shape.

Her **vivid** description of the adventure made it feel like we were there with her.

Let's Practice Spelling the Word

in reinforce	re - in - force ⟶
ou **ce** source	source ⟶
an **ible** tangible	tan - gi - ble ⟶
que unique	u - nique ⟶
vi vivid	viv - id ⟶

Now write each word in full.

reinforce		⟶
source		⟶
tangible		⟶
unique		⟶
vivid		⟶

	→	
	→	
	→	
	→	
	→	

	→	
	→	
	→	
	→	
	→	

Synonyms Puzzle 8

```
V M Q W O I Q G Z D A I X X V R P L I S
I H G U B R I G H T T A Q M P H G W T S
V T D T A H Z T Q Z X G A S K C F R Q U
I T E G M B S C R W T T B D V X E H H E
D F A V B D W S B K E K P P O N U W Y K
G Z N I Z S E U N R Z M Y W G A K G L T
I T P J C G O Q I W G D Q T M Q I K A B
V C S X T A A T U D W H R O P F N W B
T N P S X P L X W J L E R H E B G D T U
V I H Y X Z S D Z Z N Y O K Y I W H N Z
S T G V F B P P C B K T R D B F X C L F
Z S P S X U U L S Q N S R L C J F L M J
V I M D G W I N O B N O E L Z V C Q L T
K D I A P Y T G U I S Q J N P K H O V J
T S A Y B E Y N R P F Z D O K F F G F N
K J H R U F T A C X N R B O Q Z O X K I
P O F Q F B B D E I G P F Z L O Y W K G
Q P I C B L N A S H H V Y O S G B T A I
X N B Y C K J U O T S L O X S L N B A R
U F R E I N F O R C E G A U J O G Z E O
```

BRIGHT   DISTINCT   MATERIAL

ORIGIN   REINFORCE   SOURCE

STRENGTHEN   TANGIBLE   UNIQUE

VIVID

Synonyms

reinforce	——————→	
source	——————→	
tangible	——————→	
unique	——————→	
vivid	——————→	

Let's Compose Sentences

Look back at the definitions and example sentences. Can you write a sentence for each of the words?

Reinforce: _____

_____

Source: _____

_____

Tangible: _____

_____

Unique: _____

_____

Vivid: _____

_____

My Notes

Lesson 9

Definitions

Exemplary: setting a great example or being an outstanding model.

Generation: people born and living during the same period.

Legacy: something valuable such as achievements, traditions or contributions that someone leaves behind, for future generations.

Musician: a person who plays musical instruments or who creates music.

Significant: something that is important, notable or having a meaningful impact.

Example Sentences

She earned the Student of the Year award for her **exemplary** behaviour in school.

The younger **generation** is more tech-savvy and knowledgeable about digital devices.

Martin Luther King Jr. left a **legacy** of respect for human rights and equality for all people.

Many **musicians** are inspired by the beauty of nature to compose music.

Penicillin was a **significant** discovery which revolutionized medicine and introduced the first widely used antibiotic.

Let's Practice Spelling the Word

Keep Going!

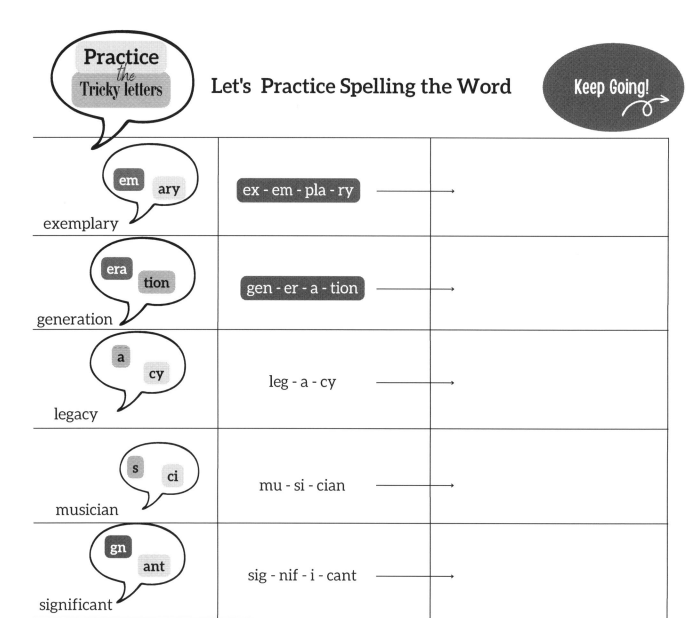

exemplary (em ary)	ex - em - pla - ry	
generation (era tion)	gen - er - a - tion	
legacy (a cy)	leg - a - cy	
musician (s ci)	mu - si - cian	
significant (gn ant)	sig - nif - i - cant	

Now write each word in full.

exemplary		
generation		
legacy		
musician		
significant		

Practice
makes
Perfect!

Synonyms Puzzle 9

```
            T  Q  Q  M
         K  W  P  W  N  U  Q  I
      P  Q  U  I  L  E  P  P  U  S  H  Y
   G  O  F  J  T  E  L  Y  R  L  D  N  W  C
   K  K  M  B  O  G  R  O  A  U  X  O  T  M
Y  Q  C  H  T  K  A  R  L  I  A  Q  I  G  U  E
P  Y  M  R  I  L  C  P  O  S  M  F  T  R  M  C
Q  W  C  O  T  P  T  Y  P  N  E  E  Y  A  W  U  O  J
W  X  H  V  M  G  N  L  C  R  W  Z  K  R  Z  S  H  N
H  U  D  E  H  K  A  M  O  L  O  P  R  E  Q  I  O  L
H  E  X  W  R  B  C  S  L  U  R  J  E  N  H  C  R  T
N  E  R  U  W  S  I  N  A  F  T  V  M  E  R  I  T  G
   U  V  I  O  M  F  K  A  G  H  S  R  G  D  A  U
   P  L  W  T  A  I  J  H  N  Y  W  O  F  A  N  W
      M  K  Q  A  N  H  N  I  Y  N  F  F  P  H
      M  W  Q  H  G  W  G  N  D  T  R  E  K  C
         E  B  C  I  E  I  A  V  Z  E  G  J
            D  S  G  E  E  D  T  P
               T  M  M  U
```

COHORT	EXEMPLARY	GENERATION
HERITAGE	LEGACY	MEANINGFUL
MUSICIAN	PERFORMER	PRAISEWORTHY
SIGNIFICANT		

Synonyms

exemplary	⟶	
generation	⟶	
legacy	⟶	
musician	⟶	
significant	⟶	

Let's Compose Sentences

Look back at the definitions and example sentences. Can you write a sentence for each of the words?

Exemplary: _____

_____

Generation: _____

_____

Legacy: _____

_____

Musician: _____

_____

Significant: _____

_____

My Notes

Lesson 10

Definitions

Audience: a group of people who watch, listen to, or attend a performance, show or presentation.

Frighten: to make someone feel scared.

Gesture: a movement of the body, especially the hands and arms, to express a feeling or convey a message.

Oblivious: not knowing, not being aware of or not paying attention to what is happening around you.

Terrific: something that is really great and wonderful.

Example Sentences

The **audience** clapped fervently at the end of the rock star's performance.

Horror movies are designed to **frighten** viewers with scenes that are full of suspense.

Her uncle **gestured** with a finger to his lips, hinting that the surprise party was a secret.

She was completely **oblivious** to the changes made to her schedule because she had been in hospital for a month.

Visiting the Space Center Houston was a **terrific** experience for the whole class.

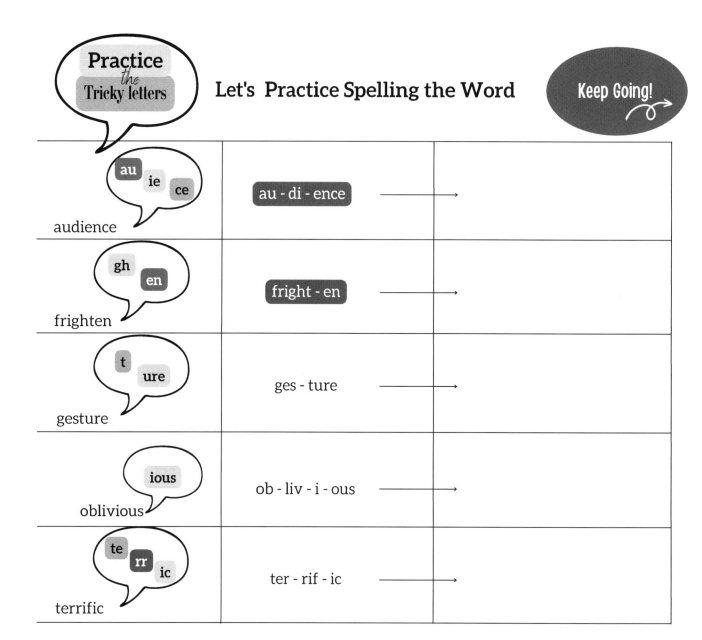

audience — au ie ce	au - di - ence →	
frighten — gh en	fright - en →	
gesture — t ure	ges - ture →	
oblivious — ious	ob - liv - i - ous →	
terrific — te rr ic	ter - rif - ic →	

Now write each word in full.

audience		→
frighten		→
gesture		→
oblivious		→
terrific		,

	→	
	→	
	→	
	→	
	→	

	→	
	→	
	→	
	→	
	→	

Synonyms Puzzle 10

```
X                                                     F
X  G                                           R  F
R  F  E                                     I  A  O
B  F  W  S                                G  N  O  D
O  H  A  A  T                             H  T  O  B  W
F  L  D  C  D  U                       T  A  J  P  L  G
W  H  C  I  I  S  R                 E  S  B  Z  Z  I  K
U  C  V  E  S  C  Y  E           N  T  P  G  K  X  V  U
N  U  V  Y  K  A  S  D  O     E  I  F  H  Q  N  V  I  H
A  R  I  P  T  R  B  L  P  S  I  C  V  S  N  M  L  X  O  A
W  B  Q  N  A  E  I  H  R  S  N  S  R  Q  D  N  A  V  U  U
A  H  M  B  V  O  W  O  A     U  B  X  Y  N  N  Z  S  O
R  K  L  K  D  W  T  C        O  E  N  K  G  R  K  E
E  U  E  R  Q  A  I              A  J  R  I  T  T  C
W  F  Z  A  T  F                    X  F  S  J  B  N
K  Y  G  C  I                          I  S  D  Q  E
Y  O  E  R                             Q  Z  N  I
W  P  R                                A  C  D
S  E                                      X  U
T                                            A
```

AUDIENCE	FANTASTIC	FRIGHTEN
GESTURE	OBLIVIOUS	SCARE
SIGNAL	SPECTATORS	TERRIFIC
UNAWARE		

Synonyms

audience	⟶
frighten	⟶
gesture	⟶
oblivious	⟶
terrific	⟶

Let's Compose Sentences

Look back at the definitions and example sentences. Can you write a sentence for each of the words?

Audience: _____

_____

Frighten: _____

_____

Gesture: _____

_____

Oblivious: _____

_____

Terrific: _____

_____

My Notes

Lesson 11

Definitions

Autumn: one of the four seasons, also know as 'fall', when the weather gets cooler and the leaves change color and fall to the ground.

Beautifully: in a way that is pleasing to the senses or exceptionally attractive.

Noticeable: standing out and catching attention.

Ingredient: a component of a recipe or a mixture.

Venture: a new and bold project, often involving new challenges or experiences.

Example Sentences

Autumn is the season to enjoy apple picking and pumpkin carving.

The vintage car, once rusted and forgotten, was restored **beautifully** by a team of dedicated enthusiasts.

The change in her hairstyle was quite **noticeable**, and everyone complimented her on it.

Flour is an essential **ingredient** in baking, used to make cakes, cookies, and bread.

Exploring the uncharted forest was a daring **venture** that tested their survival skills.

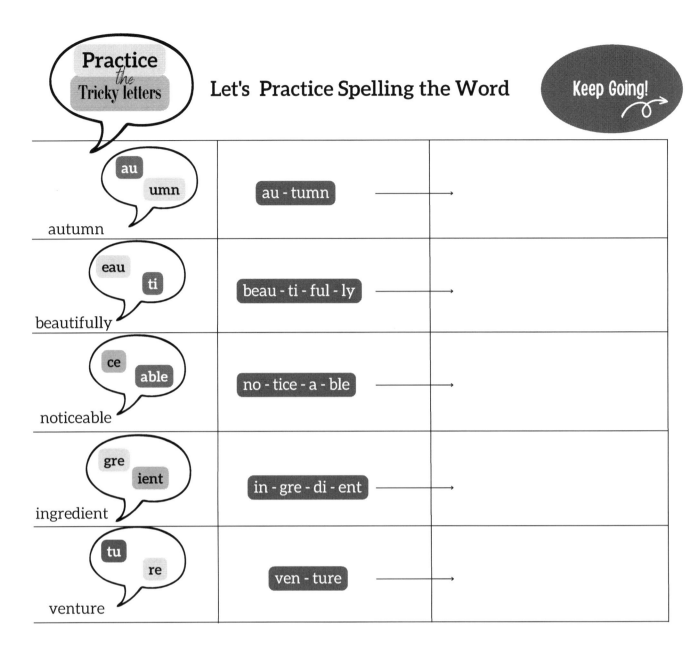

au / umn — autumn	au - tumn →	
eau / ti — beautifully	beau - ti - ful - ly →	
ce / able — noticeable	no - tice - a - ble →	
gre / ient — ingredient	in - gre - di - ent →	
tu / re — venture	ven - ture →	

Now write each word in full.

autumn	→	
beautifully	→	
noticeable	→	
ingredient	→	
venture	→	

	→	
	→	
	→	
	→	
	→	

	→	
	→	
	→	
	→	
	→	

Synonyms Puzzle 11

```
                  P   A
              W   U   R   O
          G   T   A   T   E   A
      W   U   S   N   V   G   T   L
  E   M   V   E   I   F   M   T   U   B
Q   N   P   I   D   Y   V   Y   R   R   S   O
K   N   F   D   E   V   H   E   V   A   I   B   X   E
R   K   W   E   N   S   H   V   N   U   C   R   F   A   L   L
N   M   I   R   T   N   A   G   N   T   C   T   L   M   L   P   E   X
M   S   V   G   G   B   F   D   L   D   U   W   I   Y   Z   G   U   V   L   Q
W   Q   N   R   L   P   R   M   M   D   R   M   V   O   V   B   Y   N   I   L
    I   P   H   V   T   E   U   M   T   E   I   E   B   I   D   K   I   L
        F   B   E   A   U   T   I   F   U   L   L   Y   A   B   L   Q
            R   Q   R   X   J   S   B   M   Z   Y   S   J   V   T
                C   O   M   P   O   N   E   N   T   L   Y   C
                    N   O   T   I   C   E   A   B   L   E
                        T   N   G   N   Q   D   H   J
                            M   I   T   A   V   O
                                M   K   C   R
                                    G   P
```

ATTRACTIVELY	AUTUMN	BEAUTIFULLY
COMPONENT	EVIDENT	FALL
INGREDIENT	NOTICEABLE	PROJECT
VENTURE		

Synonyms

autumn	⟶	
beautifully	⟶	
noticeable	⟶	
ingredient	⟶	
venture	⟶	

Let's Compose Sentences

Look back at the definitions and example sentences. Can you write a sentence for each of the words?

Autumn: _____

_____

Beautifully: _____

_____

Noticeable: _____

_____

Ingredient: _____

_____

Venture: _____

_____

My Notes

Lesson 12

Definitions

Official:	(i) something approved or authorized as proper or legitimate. (ii) A person with a specific role in an organization or government.
Persuade:	to convince someone by using reasons and arguments, to make them agree with you.
Realistic:	seeing things the way they truly are and making decisions based on what's likely to happen.
Solution:	a way to solve a problem or fix something that is not working.
Verify:	to check if something is true or correct.

Example Sentences

(i) The **official** announcements of the election results will be made tomorrow.
(ii) The government **official** announced new policies to address environmental concerns.

She tried to **persuade** her friends to join the book club by sharing the exciting stories they'd read together, sitting on comfy cushions, and indulging in chocolate milk and cookies.

He decided that he would set **realistic** goals to gradually improved his grades.

The **solution** to overcrowded classrooms was to extend the school building into the school yard and hire more teachers.

Border protection officers have the duty to **verify** the identity of all the travelers crossing a border to the United States.

Let's Practice Spelling the Word

Keep Going!

ff **cial** official	of - fi - cial ⟶
sua persuade	per - suade ⟶
al realistic	re - al - is - tic ⟶
tion solution	so - lu - tion ⟶
ify verify	ver - i - fy ⟶

Now write each word in full.

official		⟶
persuade		⟶
realistic		⟶
solution		⟶
verify		⟶

	→→	
	→→	
	→→	
	→→	
	→→	

	→→	
	→→	
	→→	
	'	
	→→	

Synonyms Puzzle 12

```
              Y  L  P  D
           J  O  R  R  L  J  W  S
        G  C  R  S  A  E  O  D  O  H  S  H
     X  I  E  E  C  E  W  A  L  K  T  N  J  M
     T  W  B  T  M  R  C  U  L  A  F  P  J  P
  T  S  D  I  A  D  J  T  V  Z  I  L  G  X  Z  M
  N  R  C  O  X  Y  I        B  S  S  U  S  L  L
A  W  A  C  D  K  O              V  C  T  A  K  T  M
O  L  W  O  P  N                 J  K  I  W  R  Q
U  F  I  N  E  G                 U  R  N  C  M  C
T  O  F  V  Q  K                 D  I  E  M  J  Y
R  R  E  I  T  D  P              I  Y  T  E  X  T  V
  A  L  N  C  M  K  R        U  T  A  D  H  C  E
  C  B  C  N  I  B  O  N  J  N  D  A  F  L  R  F
     I  E  M  G  A  U  T  L  I  U  Z  A  I  N
     U  G  Z  W  X  L  P  L  S  U  M  F  J  U
        M  V  O  G  E  A  R  W  R  Y  K  J
           I  Z  V  E  F  O  Q  G
              P  Z  F  B
```

ANSWER	CONVINCE	FORMAL
OFFICIAL	PERSUADE	PRACTICAL
REALISTIC	SOLUTION	VALIDATE
VERIFY		

Synonyms

official	⟶	
persuade	⟶	
realistic	⟶	
solution	⟶	
verify	⟶	

Let's Compose Sentences

Look back at the definitions and example sentences. Can you write a sentence for each of the words?

Official:
_____

_____

Persuade:
_____

_____

Realistic:
_____

_____

Solution:
_____

_____

Verify:
_____

_____

My Notes

Lesson 13

Definitions

Believe: to have faith in something as being true or real, even if you cannot prove it.

Habitat: the natural home or environment of a plant or animal.

Independent: able to do things and make decisions on your own.

Migrate: to move from one place to another, usually to find food or to a warmer climate (animals), or to find a job or better way of living (people).

Timid: shy, easily frightened or not very confident in new or unfamiliar situations.

Example Sentences

She didn't **believe** in ghosts, but the spooky noises in the old house made her a bit nervous.

The rainforest is the **habitat** of many colorful birds and exotic animals.

As he grew older, he became more **independent** and required less help from his mother for school work.

(i) The ruby-throated hummingbird **migrates** from North America to Central America during the fall, seeking a warmer climate and abundant food sources.
(ii) Many European citizens **migrate** to other EU member states in search of a better job and improved living standards.

The **timid** puppy hid under the table when strangers came to visit.

Let's Practice Spelling the Word

Keep Going!

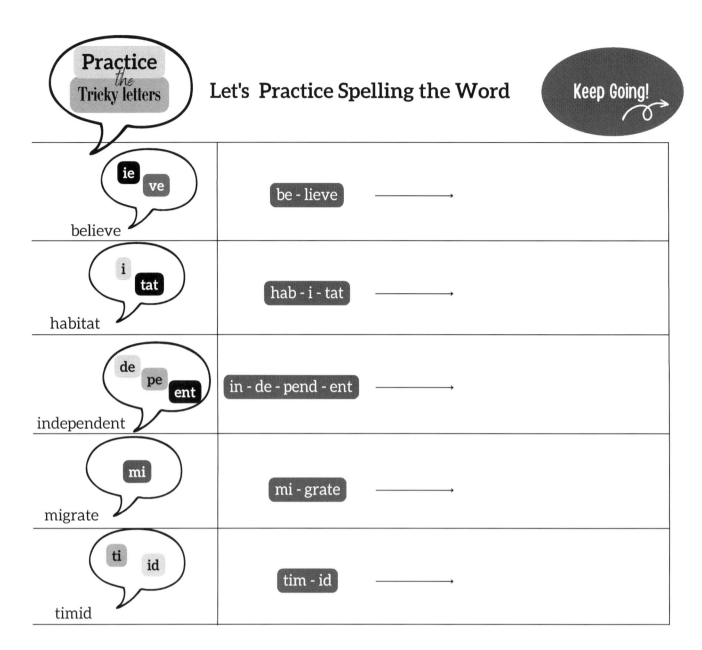

believe	be - lieve ⟶
habitat	hab - i - tat ⟶
independent	in - de - pend - ent ⟶
migrate	mi - grate ⟶
timid	tim - id ⟶

Now write each word in full.

believe		⟶
habitat		⟶
independent		⟶
migrato		⟶
timid		⟶

Practice
makes
Perfect!

	→	
	→	
	→	
	→	
	→	

	→	
	→	
	→	
	→	
	→	

Synonyms Puzzle 13

```
      F  X  T  O  U  Z                    E  O  I  X  E  L
   Z  P  I  R  H  I  O  F              J  M  X  E  W  Q  Y  A
   Y  I  M  U  N  Q  K  R  A        E  O  W  X  F  F  Z  U  B
   Y  E  Y  S  A  M  T  G  D  L  X  W  U  A  R  C  T  E  B
   M  E  E  T  G  W  S  E  I  U  E  K  E  O  B  Z  O  L  B  G
   Q  O  N  L  E  U  G  N  T  F  C  G  J  A  A  N  I  X  E  Q
   Z  G  Y  V  X  T  I  M  I  D  J  U  T  L  O  E  X  U  P  B
   O  H  Z  S  I  L  F  F  P  Q  W  L  R  M  V  U  Z  E  D  I
   I  R  X  O  X  R  G  G  N  Z  H  J  O  E  U  W  E  N  N  H
   I  F  V  P  M  E  O  L  M  D  D  U  P  E  O  E  H  D  B  A
   A  E  S  V  S  Q  X  N  Q  N  S  N  F  O  U  Y  E  F  U  Q
      V  G  C  X  O  U  L  M  L  A  G  M  J  V  P  L  Y  J
         R  E  L  O  C  A  T  E  U  X  T  K  E  M  K  M
            W  J  G  B  Z  E  P  N  K  E  N  I  O  W
               H  A  B  I  T  A  T  T  D  G  I  F
                  K  G  S  O  X  S  E  R  S  A
                     S  A  Q  B  N  A  I  M
                        J  N  T  T  Y  I
                           H  E  H  W
                              S  K
```

AUTONOMOUS	BELIEVE	ENVIRONMENT
HABITAT	INDEPENDENT	MIGRATE
RELOCATE	SHY	TIMID
TRUST		

Synonyms

believe	———————→
habitat	———————→
independent	———————→
migrate	———————→
timid	———————→

Let's Compose Sentences

Look back at the definitions and example sentences. Can you write a sentence for each of the words?

Believe: _____

_____

Habitat: _____

_____

Independent: _____

_____

Migrate: _____

_____

Timid: _____

_____

My Notes

Lesson 14

Definitions

Canyon:	a deep, narrow valley with steep sides, often carved by a river or erosion.
Edition:	a particular version or issue of a book, magazine, or other publication.
Noisy:	making a lot of loud or disruptive sounds.
Plumber:	a skilled person who installs, repairs and maintains pipes or fixtures.
Strenuous:	involving hard work and physical or mental effort.

Example Sentences

We hiked down into the deep **canyon**, surrounded by towering cliffs on either side.

The latest **edition** of the encyclopedia includes updated information on space exploration.

The construction site next door was incredibly **noisy**, with the constant sounds of machinery and tools.

The **plumber** arrived promptly and quickly repaired the burst pipe in the basement.

The athlete's **strenuous** training regimen prepared her for the challenging competition ahead.

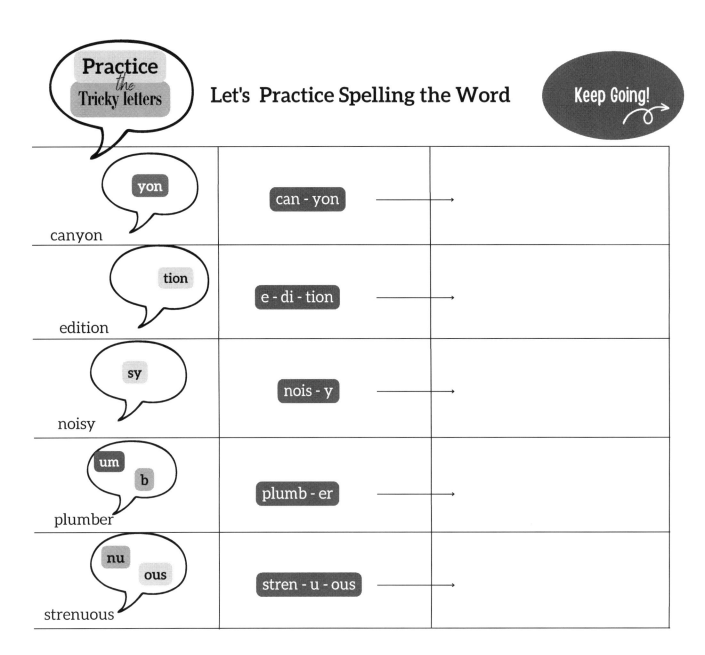

canyon (yon)	can - yon	→
edition (tion)	e - di - tion	→
noisy (sy)	nois - y	→
plumber (um) (b)	plumb - er	→
strenuous (nu) (ous)	stren - u - ous	→

Now write each word in full.

canyon		→
edition		→
noisy		→
plumber		→
strenuous		→

Practice makes Perfect!

	→	
	→	
	→	
	→	
	→	

	→	
	→	
	→	
	→	
	→	

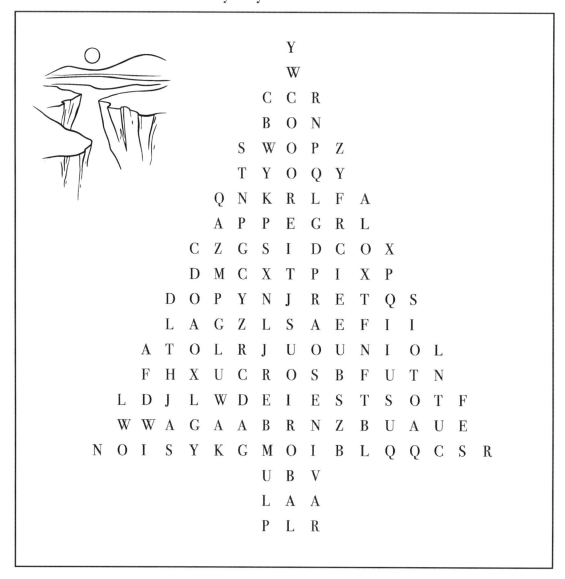

```
                      Y
                      W
              C   C   R
              B   O   N
          S   W   O   P   Z
          T   Y   O   Q   Y
      Q   N   K   R   L   F   A
      A   P   P   E   G   R   L
  C   Z   G   S   I   D   C   O   X
  D   M   C   X   T   P   I   X   P
D   O   P   Y   N   J   R   E   T   Q   S
L   A   G   Z   L   S   A   E   F   I   I
A   T   O   L   R   J   U   O   U   N   I   O   L
F   H   X   U   C   R   O   S   B   F   U   T   N
L   D   J   L   W   D   E   I   E   S   T   S   O   T   F
W   W   A   G   A   A   B   R   N   Z   B   U   A   U   E
N   O   I   S   Y   K   G   M   O   I   B   L   Q   Q   C   S   R
                      U   B   V
                      L   A   A
                      P   L   R
```

CANYON	COPY	EDITION
LABORIOUS	LOUD	NOISY
PIPEFITTER	PLUMBER	RAVINE
STRENUOUS		

Synonyms

canyon	⟶
edition	⟶
noisy	⟶
plumber	⟶
strenuous	⟶

Let's Compose Sentences

Look back at the definitions and example sentences. Can you write a sentence for each of the words?

Canyon: _____

_____

Edition: _____

_____

Noisy: _____

_____

Plumber: _____

_____

Strenuous: _____

_____

My Notes

Lesson 15

Definitions

Concentration: the act of paying close attention to something or focusing your mind on a particular task or activity.

Denominator: the bottom part of a fraction.

Fierce: showing a strong and intense determination, often in a way that appears aggressive.

Halves: two equal parts that together make one whole.

Lawyer: a professional who practices law and provides legal advice or representation to clients in legal matters, such as in court cases.

Example Sentences

We bought grandma a word search puzzle book with the hope that it would help her improve her **concentration**.

In the fraction $\frac{3}{4}$, "4" is the **denominator**, representing the total number of equal parts.

The competition between the two teams was **fierce**, with both sides giving their all.

She cut the apple into **halves**, so each person could have an equal portion.

When faced with a legal issue, it's important to consult a qualified **lawyer** for advice.

Let's Practice Spelling the Word

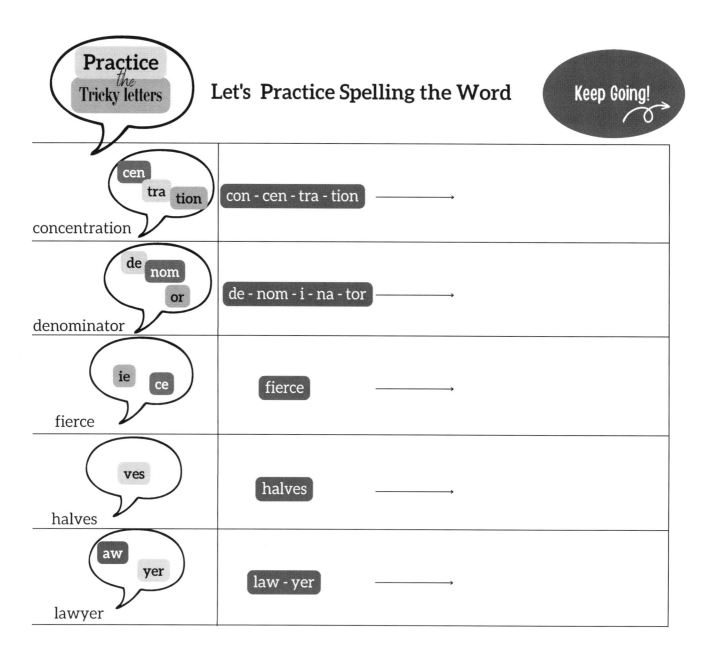

	concentration · con - cen - tra - tion ⟶
	denominator · de - nom - i - na - tor ⟶
	fierce ⟶
	halves ⟶
	lawyer · law - yer ⟶

Now write each word in full.

concentration	⟶
denominator	⟶
fierce	⟶
halves	⟶
lawyer	⟶

Practice makes Perfect!

Synonyms Puzzle 15

```
X M V D E N O M I N A T O R Q E C K K H
E F X W L N D Y U F D A A B C V J S A J
B B X F X P W P U E D P N V M F I L E B
G Z L C T N P L G U P F D I Q F V B Y O
P C T O J U C I A X D C G P E E G G C T
H M S N N D H M R M Y D R Z S B W R H T
K C E C V K E E A P B I V F X Y A T S O
C J D E G J V W D D B V N M V Z H H R M
B Z V N G H Z N N C M I G S H S I J Y N
M C O T T P X K F O H S V L F L E F K U
Q F Z R D A G T N E A I Y T E Y P D Q M
N W Z A P E F N V U V O K K F S K E Z B
Y U S T X P J I I O B N Z K R E F V R E
E K J I V W S N O O G S K U P T O P P R
N M M O B S I F K U G S G R I E C E P C
R W E N E A U P L H O Z E H W C U E P E
O K W R V W N C L F F Y C A W R S P B Y
T T G K S Y M G H U W S V G K E H Y K B
T G Y G K G A Q K A L B Z M G I Z L V B
A V B F G N M E L X E Q D I D F W D X I
```

AGGRESSIVE   ATTORNEY   BOTTOM NUMBER

CONCENTRATION   DENOMINATOR   DIVISIONS

FIERCE   FOCUS   HALVES

LAWYER

Synonyms

concentration	⟶
denominator	⟶
fierce	⟶
halves	⟶
lawyer	⟶

Let's Compose Sentences

Look back at the definitions and example sentences. Can you write a sentence for each of the words?

Concentration: _____

_____

Denominator: _____

_____

Fierce: _____

_____

Halves: _____

_____

Lawyer: _____

_____

My Notes

Lesson 16

Definitions

Descendant: someone who comes from a line of family members, like a grandchild or great-grandchild.

Formula: a special set of instructions or rules to solve a particular problem, often in math or science.

Grief: a deep and strong feeling of sadness, especially when someone you love has passed away.

Hilarious: very funny.

Inquire: to ask questions or look for information to learn more about something.

Example Sentences

The **descendants** of the last Africans who were brought to America as slaves commemorated the 162nd anniversary of the arrival of the slave ship.

When you have a math test, it's essential to remember the **formulas** for finding areas and volumes of shapes.

After losing her beloved pet dog, she experienced deep **grief** and missed him every day.

The silly antics of the clown at the circus were absolutely **hilarious**.

She decided to **inquire** about volunteering opportunities at the local animal shelter.

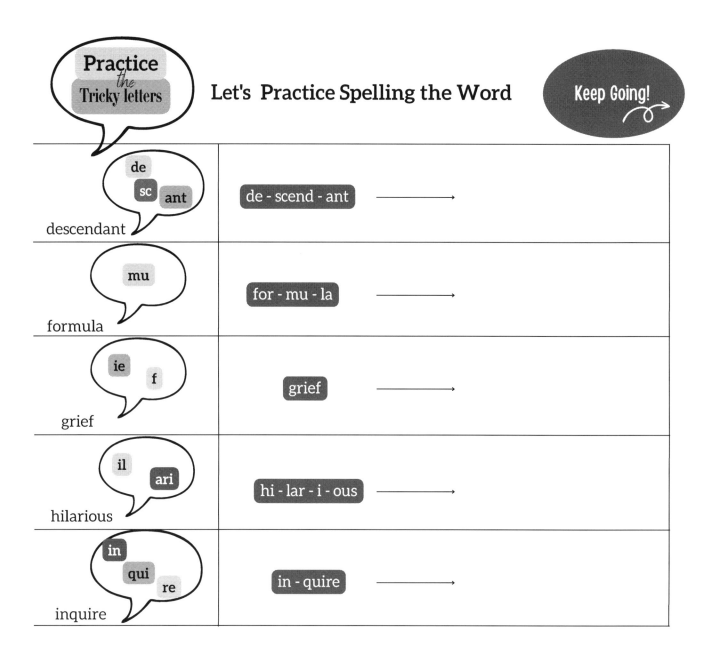

de / sc / ant descendant	de - scend - ant ⟶
mu formula	for - mu - la ⟶
ie / f grief	grief ⟶
il / ari hilarious	hi - lar - i - ous ⟶
in / qui / re inquire	in - quire ⟶

Now write each word in full.

descendant		⟶
formula		⟶
grief		⟶
hilarious		⟶
inquire		⟶

	→	
	→	
	→	
	→	
	→	

	→	
	→	
	→	
	→	
	→	

Synonyms Puzzle 16

```
                    S  H  A  F
                 K  Q  L  L  O  K  V  T
              O  U  F  D  T  R  H  M  G  C  U  N
           W  F  A  E  U  M  E  M  P  R  R  Z  I  S
           X  F  Z  Y  U  M  R  N  E  J  V  I  O  C
        B  L  S  U  L  T  K  W  M  P  S  U  R  E  F  R
        H  H  P  A  X  Q  K  D  B  F  T  R  C  J  F  B
     U  O  D  R  I  W  W  V  I  K  Q  O  U  F  C  S  N  J
     B  K  O  I  F  U  M  Y  F  S  W  K  I  U  G  Q  P  G
     N  P  H  N  D  E  S  C  E  N  D  A  N  T  M  R  Q  F
     A  T  T  G  Z  E  C  V  T  S  P  M  Y  W  B  S  U  E
     T  S  E  E  K  G  A  K  Q  U  I  H  U  X  K  W  R  S
        J  M  Y  T  Q  V  E  R  O  I  N  L  G  L  I  I
        Z  N  M  W  G  C  B  I  H  I  O  W  U  C  J
           U  E  E  K  I  F  Y  R  K  R  V  Q  W  L
           K  N  S  B  X  L  N  A  J  U  N  S  U  E
              A  W  U  H  H  N  L  K  I  F  F  Y
                 J  L  D  U  I  K  C  K
                    I  F  H  G
```

ASK	DESCENDANT	FORMULA
FUNNY	GRIEF	HILARIOUS
INQUIRE	METHOD	OFFSPRING
SORROW		

Synonyms

descendant	⟶	
formula	⟶	
grief	⟶	
hilarious	⟶	
inquire	⟶	

Let's Compose Sentences

Look back at the definitions and example sentences. Can you write a sentence for each of the words?

Descendant: _____

_____

Formula: _____

_____

Grief: _____

_____

Hilarious: _____

_____

Inquire: _____

_____

My Notes

Lesson 17

Definitions

Hop: to jump with one or both feet.

League: a group of individuals or teams that come together for a common purpose or to participate in a particular activity, such as sports or community service.

Nurture: to care for, support, and encourage the growth and development of someone or something, providing love, attention, and guidance.

Obedient: willing to follow rules, orders, or instructions.

Physical: related to the body or the world.

Example Sentences

In the game of hopscotch, you must **hop** from one square to another without stepping on the lines.

Teams of different skill levels are allowed to participate in our school's basketball **league**, making it very inclusive.

Teachers aim to **nurture** the curiosity of their students by encouraging questions and exploration.

The **obedient** German Shepherd faithfully followed the instructions of the detective and was able to retrieve crucial evidence for the investigation.

During the **physical** exam, the doctor checked the patient's heartbeat, reflexes, and overall health.

Practice the Tricky letters

Let's Practice Spelling the Word

Keep Going!

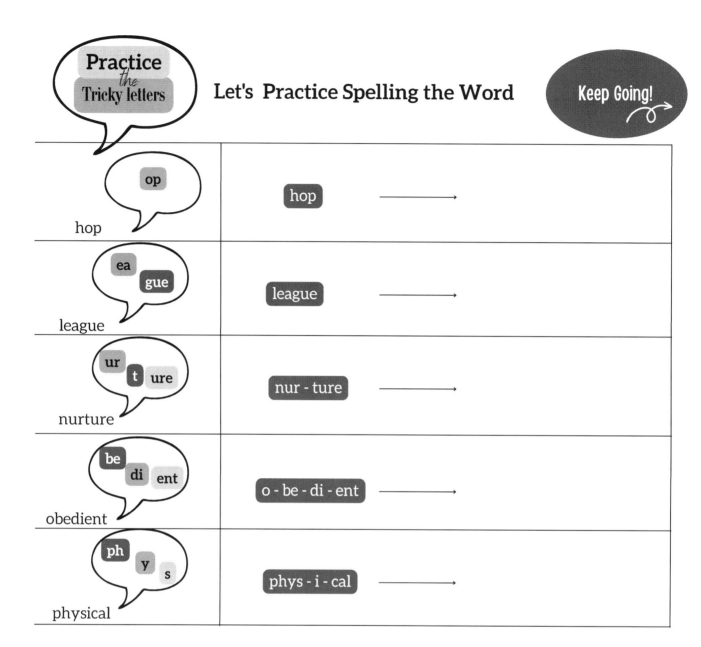

hop	hop ⟶
league	league ⟶
nurture	nur - ture ⟶
obedient	o - be - di - ent ⟶
physical	phys - i - cal ⟶

Now write each word in full.

hop		⟶
league		⟶
nurture		⟶
obedient		⟶
physical		⟶

Practice makes Perfect!

	→	
	→	
	→	
	→	
	→	

	→	
	→	
	→	
	→	
	→	

```
A                                                               U
S   F                                              Q   B
S   S   O                                       P   O   L
O   Q   E   S                                   H   D   E   I
C   T   D   F   T                           U   I   A   E   J
I   U   Y   N   U   E                   Z   L   G   Q   Z   N
A   S   W   G   J   K   R           L   Y   U   Z   U   U   V
T   T   M   B   C   Q   X   O       R   P   E   F   S   R   J   H
I   B   N   P   X   A   P   X   G   A   B   B   W   J   T   C   V   H
O   M   E   O   T   Y   N   P   I   M   B   D   C   S   Z   U   H   Z   R   H
N   P   X   Z   C   O   M   P   L   I   A   N   T   W   R   M   R   B   E   V
S   F   T   N   J   O   F   M   I           Z   B   E   X   P   G   K   V   L
A   C   W   H   O   P   Q   L           P   S   I   S   H   Q   I   T
T   M   F   Q   W   F   A               K   L   W   G   M   J   N
Y   S   P   T   T   C                   N   E   F   Z   E   E
S   C   P   Y   I                       M   T   A   H   I
Q   X   C   S                           E   Q   B   D
M   G   Y                               P   W   E
D   H                                   L   B
P                                       O
```

ASSOCIATION	BODILY	COMPLIANT
FOSTER	HOP	JUMP
LEAGUE	NURTURE	OBEDIENT
PHYSICAL		

Synonyms

hop	⟶
league	⟶
nurture	⟶
obedient	⟶
physical	⟶

Let's Compose Sentences

Look back at the definitions and example sentences. Can you write a sentence for each of the words?

Hop: _____

_____

League: _____

_____

Nurture: _____

_____

Obedient: _____

_____

Physical: _____

_____

My Notes

Lesson 18

Definitions

Occur: when something happens or takes place.

Priority: something considered to be the most important or comes first in a list of things to do.

Rebel: a person who goes against authority or against what is considered normal.

Repetition: the act of doing or say something over and over again.

Vacuum: an empty space or a situation where something is missing or lacking.

Example Sentences

Many accidents **occur** on the road because people don't follow traffic rules.

She had a list of things to do in preparation for the ceremony, but she gave **priority** to the seating protocol.

He's known for his independent spirit and willingness to **rebel** against unfair rules.

Learning a new language requires regular **repetition** of vocabulary and phrases.

In the quiet of the night, there was a sense of **vacuum** as the city slept, and the streets were empty.

Let's Practice Spelling the Word

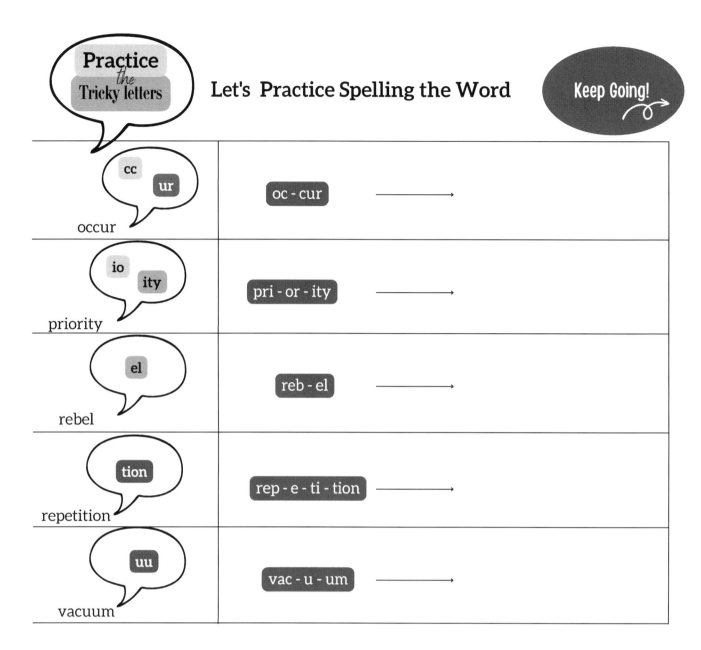

cc **ur** occur	oc - cur ⟶
io **ity** priority	pri - or - ity ⟶
el rebel	reb - el ⟶
tion repetition	rep - e - ti - tion ⟶
uu vacuum	vac - u - um ⟶

Now write each word in full.

occur		⟶
priority		⟶
rebel		⟶
repetition		⟶
vacuum		⟶

	→	
	→	
	→	
	→	
	→	

	→	
	→	
	→	
	→	
	→	

Synonyms Puzzle 18

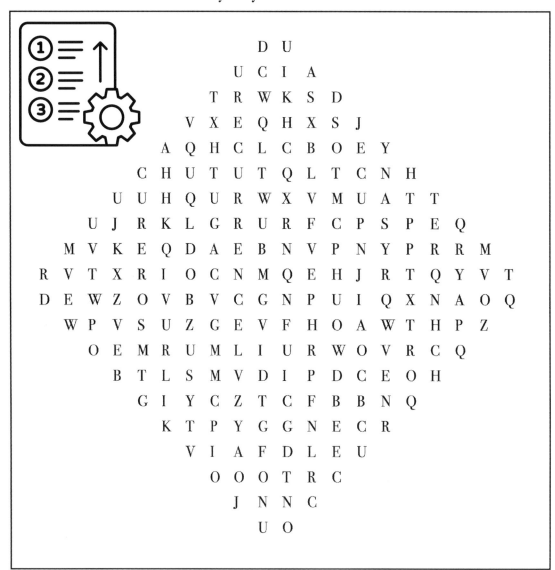

```
              D  U
           U  C  I  A
        T  R  W  K  S  D
        V  X  E  Q  H  X  S  J
     A  Q  H  C  L  C  B  O  E  Y
     C  H  U  T  U  T  Q  L  T  C  N  H
  U  U  H  Q  U  R  W  X  V  M  U  A  T  T
  U  J  R  K  L  G  R  U  R  F  C  P  S  P  E  Q
M  V  K  E  Q  D  A  E  B  N  V  P  N  Y  P  R  R  M
R  V  T  X  R  I  O  C  N  M  Q  E  H  J  R  T  Q  Y  V  T
D  E  W  Z  O  V  B  V  C  G  N  P  U  I  Q  X  N  A  O  Q
  W  P  V  S  U  Z  G  E  V  F  H  O  A  W  T  H  P  Z
     O  E  M  R  U  M  L  I  U  R  W  O  V  R  C  Q
        B  T  L  S  M  V  D  I  P  D  C  E  O  H
           G  I  Y  C  Z  T  C  F  B  B  N  Q
              K  T  P  Y  G  G  N  E  C  R
                 V  I  A  F  D  L  E  U
                    O  O  O  T  R  C
                       J  N  N  C
                          U  O
```

DISSENTER	HAPPEN	OCCUR
PRIORITY	REBEL	RECURRENCE
REPETITION	TOP CONCERN	VACUUM
VOID		

Synonyms

occur	⟶
priority	⟶
rebel	⟶
repetition	⟶
vacuum	⟶

Let's Compose Sentences

Look back at the definitions and example sentences. Can you write a sentence for each of the words?

Occur:

_____

_____

Priority:

_____

_____

Rebel:

_____

_____

Repetition:

_____

_____

Vacuum:

_____

_____

My Notes

Lesson 19

Definitions

Luminous: giving off light, brightness, or a glow.

Mention: to bring up or speak about something briefly.

Muscle: a strong, fibrous tissue in the body that helps with bodily movements.

Numerator: the top part of a fraction.

Quest: a journey or search undertaken to achieve a significant goal, find something valuable, or overcome challenges.

Example Sentences

At the news that she had been accepted to her preferred college, her face became **luminous** with happiness.

Can you please **mention** the meeting time in your email so everyone knows when to join?

Overtraining led to a strained **muscle**, requiring the athlete to take an extended break from training, for therapy and recovery.

In the fraction $\frac{1}{6}$, "1" is the **numerator**, representing how many parts you have, out of 6 parts.

His personal **quest** was to overcome his fears and become a confident public speaker.

Let's Practice Spelling the Word

Keep Going!

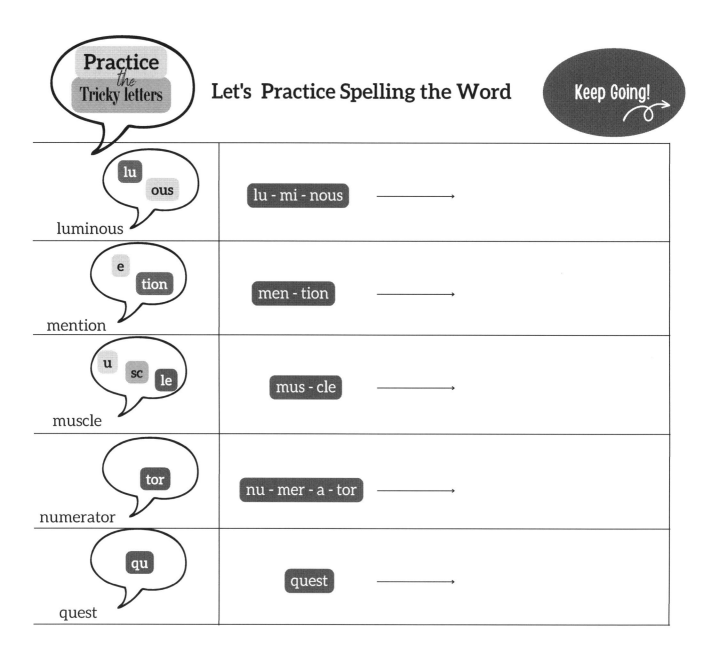

luminous	lu - mi - nous	⟶
mention	men - tion	⟶
muscle	mus - cle	⟶
numerator	nu - mer - a - tor	⟶
quest	quest	⟶

Now write each word in full.

luminous		⟶
mention		⟶
muscle		⟶
numerator		⟶
quest		⟶

Practice
makes
Perfect!

	→	
	→	
	→	
	→	
	→	

	→	
	→	
	→	
	→	
	→	

Synonyms Puzzle 19

```
            T  I  V  A
         H  Z  G  V  C  Q  W  B
      L  X  E  L  M  T  O  J  R  K  D  C
   F  G  L  N  B  U  T  N  I  W  O  N  M  I
   K  C  O  M  O  I  M  N  L  G  G  Z  E  U
G  S  G  B  Z  Y  O  G  I  V  Q  L  P  N  Q  Q
U  E  B  H  V  N  U        N  I  L  P  T  U  P
M  T  X  W  L  K  P           O  B  K  I  E  O  Q
N  U  P  T  X  H              U  L  O  S  A  S
M  B  E  O  L  P              Y  S  N  T  U  M
U  C  D  P  T  M              V  R  J  U  A  R
Z  J  I  N  T  M  W        J  B  I  E  U  O  K
   H  T  U  C  O  G  O     E  N  Q  M  J  T  S
   R  I  M  C  S  L  S  K  J  F  F  T  A  A  E  B
      O  B  R  U  E  W  F  F  M  H  U  R  U  J
      N  E  Y  C  P  M  N  S  G  L  E  S  W  O
         R  G  C  W  Y  W  I  D  M  S  J  R
         R  K  B  R  N  U  I  Y
            B  B  N  T
```

BRIGHT	BRING UP	EXPEDITION
LUMINOUS	MENTION	MUSCLE
NUMERATOR	QUEST	TISSUE
TOP NUMBER		

Synonyms

luminous	⟶	
mention	⟶	
muscle	⟶	
numerator	⟶	
quest	⟶	

Let's Compose Sentences

Look back at the definitions and example sentences. Can you write a sentence for each of the words?

Luminous:

_____

_____

Mention:

_____

_____

Muscle:

_____

_____

Numerator:

_____

_____

Quest:

_____

_____

My Notes

Lesson 20

Definitions

Ferocious: very wild, fierce and aggressive.

Keen: having a strong interest in, or desire for, something.

Knack: a natural skill or talent for doing something very well, often with ease.

Quaint: old-fashioned, charming or picturesque.

Temptation: a strong urge or desire to do something, especially when it's not good for you.

Example Sentences

The **ferocious** roar, echoing through the jungle, signaled to the puma that it had inadvertently encroached upon the jaguar's territory.

She has a **keen** interest in story-writing so she signed up for a writer's course for beginners.

His **knack** for solving puzzles helped him win the crossword competition.

The **quaint** little cottage in the woods looked like something from a fairy tale.

The **temptation** to eat the entire chocolate cake was hard to resist.

Practice the Tricky letters

Let's Practice Spelling the Word

Keep Going!

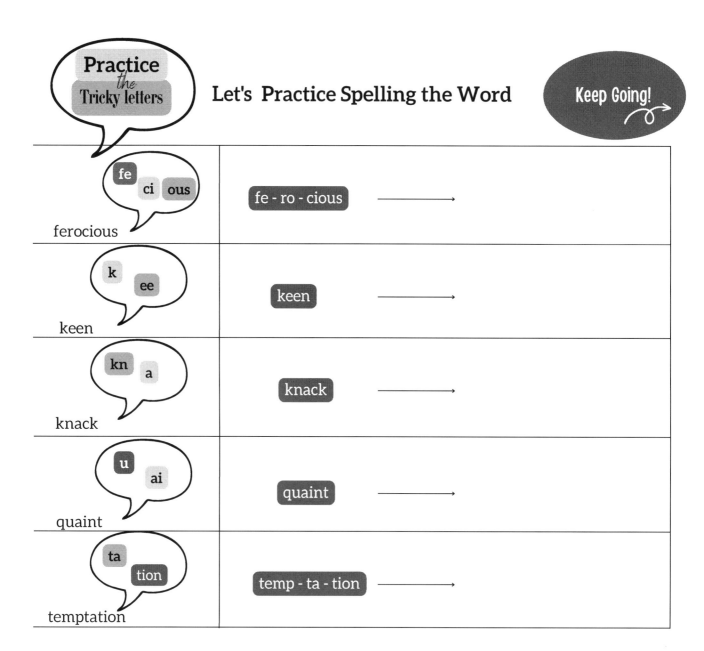

ferocious	fe - ro - cious ⟶
keen	keen ⟶
knack	knack ⟶
quaint	quaint ⟶
temptation	temp - ta - tion ⟶

Now write each word in full.

ferocious		⟶
keen		⟶
knack		⟶
quaint		
temptation		⟶

Practice makes Perfect!

	→	
	→	
	→	
	→	
	→	

	→	
	→	
	→	
	→	
	→	

```
G                                                   J
Y  X                                          D  I
F  U  Y                                  A  N  O
N  E  I  K                               Q  T  T  L
P  T  R  D  E                         S  E  Y  A  D
C  F  K  O  E  E                   V  R  U  W  L  F
L  H  A  Q  C  X  N             D  E  V  W  O  E  A
K  O  B  W  X  I  N  J       Y  S  Q  W  K  H  N  S
U  Y  P  U  O  U  O  X  J  K  T  X  A  H  I  V  T  H
V  S  D  N  W  S  Q  U  X  X  X  E  D  N  T  L  U  X  B  I
X  L  H  G  T  L  R  X  S  N  D  T  E  E  D  H  U  O  L  O
B  M  S  S  T  I  J  Q  O        C  X  I  X  S  T  R  O  N
K  N  A  C  K  R  X  I           Z  U  V  D  V  T  E  E
S  P  G  L  Y  Q  T              J  F  F  A  N  P  D
K  K  S  B  B  A                 F  W  O  I  B  E
A  M  W  E  T                    N  B  A  J  G
I  V  D  P                       N  U  V  A
D  W  M                          Q  A  V  S
H  E                             O     A
T                                      S
```

FEROCIOUS	INTERESTED	KEEN
KNACK	LURE	OLD-FASHIONED
QUAINT	SAVAGE	TALENT
TEMPTATION		

Synonyms

ferocious	———→
keen	———→
knack	———→
quaint	———→
temptation	———→

Let's Compose Sentences

Look back at the definitions and example sentences. Can you write a sentence for each of the words?

Ferocious: _____

_____

Keen: _____

_____

Knack: _____

_____

Quaint: _____

_____

Temptation: _____

_____

My Notes

Assessment Quizzes

Assessment: Lessons 1-2

Next to or adjoining something else.
(a) adjasent
(b) adjecent
(c) adjacent

To gain or obtain possession of something.
(a) aquire
(b) acquire
(c) acqwire

Past participle of "blow," meaning carried or moved by the wind, or destroyed.
(a) blown
(b) blowne
(c) blone

A state of accepting something as true or real.
(a) beleef
(b) beleaf
(c) belief

A sudden and widespread disaster, often resulting in significant damage or loss.
(a) catastrophy
(b) catastrofee
(c) catastrophe

A relationship in which a person or thing is linked or associated with another.
(a) connection
(b) conection
(c) connectcion

Causing great damage, harm, or suffering.
(a) disastrous
(b) disastrious
(c) disastreous

Extremely bright, impressive, or striking.
(a) dazzling
(b) dazeling
(c) dazzeling

An imaginary line that circles the Earth, dividing it into the Northern Hemisphere and the Southern Hemisphere.
(a) iquator
(b) equator
(c) equater

To represent (something) as being larger, better, or worse than it actually is.
(a) exegerate
(b) exaggerate
(c) exagerate

SCORE   /10

Assessment: Lessons 3-4

Select the correct word.

Having existed for a very long time.
(a) anecint
(b) anceint
(c) ancient

A main branch of a tree, especially one of the larger branches.
(a) bow
(b) bough
(c) bouwgh

Providing physical ease and relaxation.
(a) comfortable
(b) conftorble
(c) confortible

The act of leaving a place or starting a journey.
(a) departare
(b) departure
(c) diparture

The act of giving someone support, confidence, or hope.
(a) encouragement
(b) encouragment
(c) encoragement

To concentrate one's attention or effort on something.
(a) focus
(b) focuss
(c) focous

The system or group of people governing a state or community.
(a) goverment
(b) govornment
(c) government

Forming a pleasing or consistent whole.
(a) harmoneous
(b) harmonious
(c) harmonieous

To supply water to (land or crops) to help growth, typically by means of channels.
(a) irrigate
(b) irigate
(c) irregate

A person who is younger or of lower rank in a group.
(a) junor
(b) junier
(c) junior

SCORE   /10

Assessment: Lessons 5-6

Easily broken or damaged.
(a) fragille
(b) fragile
(c) fragil

To look steadily and intently, especially in admiration, surprise, or thought.
(a) gaze
(b) gase
(c) gaize

To participate in an activity or be part of something.
(a) involv
(b) involve
(c) invoulve

Cheerful, friendly, and full of high spirits.
(a) joviel
(b) joviale
(c) jovial

Information and skills acquired through experience, education, or training.
(a) nowledge
(b) knowlege
(c) knowledge

A complex and intricate network of passages.
(a) labyrinth
(b) labirinth
(c) labirynth

A figure of speech in which a word or phrase is used to describe something to which it is not literally applicable.
(a) metaphour
(b) methaphor
(c) metaphor

To give a spoken or written account of events or a story.
(a) narate
(b) narrate
(c) nerrate

The point or place where something begins.
(a) oregin
(b) origin
(c) origine

Strange or unusual.
(a) peculier
(b) peculiar
(c) peculliar

SCORE   /10

Assessment: Lessons 7-8

Select the correct word.

To use the exact words of someone else in writing or speaking.

(a) qoute
(b) quoet
(c) quote

To get or bring (something) back.

(a) retreive
(b) retrieve
(c) retrive

A person or thing that takes the place of another.

(a) substitute
(b) substitut
(c) substetut

A supposition or a system of ideas intended to explain something.

(a) theorie
(b) teory
(c) theory

Applicable or common to all.

(a) universel
(b) universall
(c) universal

To strengthen or support with additional materials or evidence.

(a) reenforce
(b) reinforce
(c) rienforce

A place, person, or thing from which something comes or can be obtained.

(a) source
(b) sourse
(c) sorce

Capable of being touched or felt.

(a) tangable
(b) tangible
(c) tangibble

Being the only one of its kind.

(a) unique
(b) uniqeu
(c) uneque

Producing powerful feelings or strong, clear images in the mind.

(a) vivid
(b) vived
(c) vevid

SCORE   /10

Assessment: Lessons 9-10

Serving as an excellent example or outstanding.
(a) exemplary
(b) exemplery
(c) examplary

All the people born and living at about the same time.
(a) generaition
(b) generation
(c) generetion

Something handed down from one generation to the next.
(a) legasy
(b) legacie
(c) legacy

A person who plays a musical instrument, especially as a profession.
(a) musisian
(b) musician
(c) musitian

Having importance or consequence; noteworthy.
(a) singificant
(b) significant
(c) significent

A group of people who gather to watch or listen to a performance, speech, or event.
(a) audiance
(b) audience
(c) audiancee

To make someone afraid or scared.
(a) frighten
(b) freghiten
(c) fryghten

A movement of part of the body, to express an idea or meaning.
(a) jesture
(b) gesteur
(c) gesture

Not aware of or not paying attention to something.
(a) oblivious
(b) oblivius
(c) obliveous

Extremely good or excellent; causing excitement or admiration.
(a) terific
(b) teriffic
(c) terrific

SCORE   /10

Assessment: Lessons 11-12

Select the correct word.

The season between summer and winter, often characterized by colorful leaves falling from trees.

(a) automn
(b) autum
(c) autumn

In an attractive manner.

(a) beatifully
(b) beautifully
(c) baeutifully

Easily seen or observed.

(a) noticable
(b) noticible
(c) noticeable

A component or element that is used in making a product or dish.

(a) ingrediant
(b) ingredient
(c) ingridient

A risky or daring journey or undertaking.

(a) venture
(b) venteur
(c) ventur

Connected with an authority or government department.

(a) offitial
(b) official
(c) oficial

To convince or influence someone to do something through reasoning or argument.

(a) persuade
(b) perswade
(c) persaude

Representing things as they are in reality; practical.

(a) realistik
(b) realistic
(c) reelistic

A method or process for dealing with a problem or challenge.

(a) solution
(b) solutian
(c) sollution

To confirm the accuracy or truth of something.

(a) verify
(b) verrify
(b) verifye

SCORE   /10

Assessment: Lessons 13-14

To accept that something is true or exists without proof.
(a) beleive
(b) believe
(c) beleeve

The natural environment in which an animal or plant lives.
(a) habitet
(b) habitant
(c) habitat

Free to make one's own decisions.
(a) independant
(b) independent
(c) indepandent

The seasonal movement of animals from one region to another.
(a) migraet
(b) migreat
(c) migrate

Shy or easily frightened.
(a) timmid
(b) timid
(c) timmed

A deep, narrow valley with steep sides, often with a stream flowing through it.
(a) canion
(b) canon
(c) canyon

A particular version of a book, magazine, or other publication.
(a) edition
(b) edician
(c) eddition

Making a lot of noise; loud and clamorous.
(a) noizy
(b) noisie
(c) noisy

A person who installs and repairs pipes and fittings for water supply or drainage.
(a) plummer
(b) plumber
(c) plumer

Requiring or involving a lot of effort and energy.
(a) strenous
(b) strenuous
(c) straneous

SCORE   /10

Assessment: Lessons 15-16

Select the correct word.

The action or power of focusing one's attention or mental effort.

(a) concentration
(b) consentration
(c) concentracian

The number below the line in a fraction.

(a) denominator
(b) denominater
(c) denomenator

Showing a heartfelt and powerful intensity.

(a) fearce
(b) fierse
(c) fierce

Plural of "half," meaning two equal parts of something.

(a) halvs
(b) halves
(c) halfs

An attorney.

(a) lawyer
(b) laywer
(c) lawiar

A person, plant, or animal that is descended from a particular ancestor.

(a) descendent
(b) descendant
(c) desendant

A mathematical rule or relationship expressed in symbols.

(a) formieula
(b) formula
(c) formeula

Deep sorrow, especially caused by someone's death.

(a) grief
(b) greif
(c) greef

Extremely funny or entertaining, causing laughter.

(a) hilairious
(b) hilerious
(c) hilarious

To seek information by asking a question.

(a) inqwire
(b) inquier
(c) inquire

SCORE   /10

Assessment: Lessons 17-18

Select the correct word.

To move by jumping on one foot.
(a) hopp
(b) hop
(c) hope

To happen or take place.
(a) occurr
(b) occure
(c) occur

A group of sports teams or organizations that compete against each other.
(a) leegue
(b) leageu
(c) league

Something that is considered more important or takes precedence over others.
(a) priority
(b) priorety
(c) pryority

To care for and encourage the growth or development of someone or something.
(a) nurteure
(b) nurture
(c) nurtuer

A person who resists or opposes authority, control, or tradition.
(a) rebel
(b) rebal
(c) rebbel

Willing to obey or follow rules and instructions.
(a) obedient
(b) obediant
(c) obiedient

The action of repeating something that has already been said or written.
(a) repetision
(b) repetition
(c) repitition

Related to the body or physical activity; tangible.
(a) fizical
(b) fysical
(c) physical

A space that is empty of matter.
(a) vaccuum
(b) vacum
(c) vacuum

SCORE   /10

Assessment: Lessons 19-20

Select the correct word.

Emitting light or shining brightly.
(a) luminous
(b) lumminous
(c) luminus

To bring something up or speak about it, usually briefly.
(a) menshion
(b) mention
(c) mansion

A tissue that is a part of the body's system for movement.
(a) mussel
(b) mucsle
(c) muscle

The number above the line in a fraction.
(a) numeraetor
(b) numerator
(c) newmerater

A long and often adventurous journey in search of something.
(a) quest
(b) qwest
(c) queste

Extremely fierce or aggressive.
(a) ferocius
(b) ferocious
(c) feroshious

Having a strong or eager interest or enthusiasm.
(a) kean
(b) keene
(c) keen

A special skill or talent for doing something easily.
(a) Gnak
(b) knack
(c) nack

Attractively old-fashioned in a charming and picturesque way.
(a) quaint
(b) qwaint
(c) queaint

The desire to do something, especially something wrong or unwise.
(a) temptation
(ab temptashun
(c) temptaetion

SCORE   /10

183

Assessment Quizzes
Answer Key

Assessment: Lessons 1-2

Select the correct word.

Next to or adjoining something else.
(a) adjasent
(b) adjecent
(c) adjacent

To gain or obtain possession of something.
(a) aquire
(b) acquire
(c) acqwire

Past participle of "blow," meaning carried or moved by the wind, or destroyed.
(a) blown
(b) blowne
(c) blone

A state of accepting something as true or real.
(a) beleef
(b) beleaf
(c) belief

A sudden and widespread disaster, often resulting in significant damage or loss.
(a) catastrophy
(b) catastrofee
(c) catastrophe

A relationship in which a person or thing is linked or associated with another.
(a) connection
(b) conection
(c) connectcion

Causing great damage, harm, or suffering.
(a) disastrous
(b) disastrious
(c) disastreous

Extremely bright, impressive, or striking.
(a) dazzling
(b) dazeling
(c) dazzeling

An imaginary line that circles the Earth, dividing it into the Northern Hemisphere and the Southern Hemisphere.
(a) iquator
(b) equator
(c) equater

To represent (something) as being larger, better, or worse than it actually is.
(a) exegerate
(b) exaggerate
(c) exagerate

SCORE   /10

Assessment: Lessons 3-4

Select the correct word.

Having existed for a very long time.
(a) anecint
(b) anceit
(c) ancient

A main branch of a tree, especially one of the larger branches.
(a) bow
(b) bough
(c) bouwgh

Providing physical ease and relaxation.
(a) comfortable
(b) conftorble
(c) confortible

The act of leaving a place or starting a journey.
(a) departare
(b) departure
(c) diparture

The act of giving someone support, confidence, or hope.
(a) encouragement
(b) encouragment
(c) encoragement

To concentrate one's attention or effort on something.
(a) focus
(b) focuss
(c) focous

The system or group of people governing a state or community.
(a) goverment
(b) govornment
(c) government

Forming a pleasing or consistent whole.
(a) harmoneous
(b) harmonious
(c) harmonieous

To supply water to (land or crops) to help growth, typically by means of channels.
(a) irrigate
(b) irigate
(c) irregate

A person who is younger or of lower rank in a group.
(a) junor
(b) junier
(c) junior

SCORE   /10

Assessment: Lessons 5-6

Select the correct word.

Easily broken or damaged.
(a) fragille
(b) fragile
(c) fragil

To look steadily and intently, especially in admiration, surprise, or thought.
(a) gaze
(b) gase
(c) gaize

To participate in an activity or be part of something.
(a) involv
(b) involve
(c) invoulve

Cheerful, friendly, and full of high spirits.
(a) joviel
(b) joviale
(c) jovial

Information and skills acquired through experience, education, or training.
(a) nowledge
(b) knowlege
(c) knowledge

A complex and intricate network of passages.
(a) labyrinth
(b) labirinth
(c) labirynth

A figure of speech in which a word or phrase is used to describe something to which it is not literally applicable.
(a) metaphour
(b) methaphor
(c) metaphor

To give a spoken or written account of events or a story.
(a) narate
(b) narrate
(c) nerrate

The point or place where something begins.
(a) oregin
(b) origin
(c) origine

Strange or unusual.
(a) peculier
(b) peculiar
(c) peculliar

SCORE   /10

Assessment: Lessons 7-8

Select the correct word.

To use the exact words of someone else in writing or speaking.
(a) qoute
(b) quoet
(c) quote

To get or bring (something) back.
(a) retreive
(b) retrieve
(c) retrive

A person or thing that takes the place of another.
(a) substitute
(b) substitut
(c) substetut

A supposition or a system of ideas intended to explain something.
(a) theorie
(b) teory
(c) theory

Applicable or common to all.
(a) universel
(b) universall
(c) universal

To strengthen or support with additional materials or evidence.
(a) reenforce
(b) reinforce
(c) rienforce

A place, person, or thing from which something comes or can be obtained.
(a) source
(b) sourse
(c) sorce

Capable of being touched or felt.
(a) tangable
(b) tangible
(c) tangibble

Being the only one of its kind.
(a) unique
(b) uniqeu
(c) uneque

Producing powerful feelings or strong, clear images in the mind.
(a) vivid
(b) vived
(c) vevid

SCORE   /10

Assessment: Lessons 9-10

Select the correct word.

Serving as an excellent example or outstanding.

(a) exemplary

(b) exemplery

(c) examplary

All the people born and living at about the same time.

(a) generaition

(b) generation

(c) generetion

Something handed down from one generation to the next.

(a) legasy

(b) legacie

(c) legacy

A person who plays a musical instrument, especially as a profession.

(a) musisian

(b) musician

(c) musitian

Having importance or consequence; noteworthy.

(a) singificant

(b) significant

(c) significent

A group of people who gather to watch or listen to a performance, speech, or event.

(a) audiance

(b) audience

(c) audiancee

To make someone afraid or scared.

(a) frighten

(b) freghiten

(c) fryghten

A movement of part of the body, to express an idea or meaning.

(a) jesture

(b) gesteur

(c) gesture

Not aware of or not paying attention to something.

(a) oblivious

(b) oblivius

(c) obliveous

Extremely good or excellent; causing excitement or admiration.

(a) terific

(b) teriffic

(c) territic

SCORE   /10

Assessment: Lessons 11-12

Select the correct word.

The season between summer and winter, often characterized by colorful leaves falling from trees.

(a) automn
(b) autum
(c) autumn

In an attractive manner.

(a) beatifully
(b) beautifully
(c) baeutifully

Easily seen or observed.

(a) noticable
(b) noticible
(c) noticeable

A component or element that is used in making a product or dish.

(a) ingrediant
(b) ingredient
(c) ingridient

A risky or daring journey or undertaking.

(a) venture
(b) venteur
(c) ventur

Connected with an authority or government department.

(a) offitial
(b) official
(c) oficial

To convince or influence someone to do something through reasoning or argument.

(a) persuade
(b) perswade
(c) persaude

Representing things as they are in reality; practical.

(a) realistik
(b) realistic
(c) reelistic

A method or process for dealing with a problem or challenge.

(a) solution
(b) solutian
(c) sollution

To confirm the accuracy or truth of something.

(a) verify
(b) verrify
(b) verifye

SCORE /10

Assessment: Lessons 13-14

To accept that something is true or exists without proof.
(a) beleive
(b) believe
(c) beleeve

A deep, narrow valley with steep sides, often with a stream flowing through it.
(a) canion
(b) canon
(c) canyon

The natural environment in which an animal or plant lives.
(a) habitet
(b) habitant
(c) habitat

A particular version of a book, magazine, or other publication.
(a) edition
(b) edician
(c) eddition

Free to make one's own decisions.
(a) independant
(b) independent
(c) indepandent

Making a lot of noise; loud and clamorous.
(a) noizy
(b) noisie
(c) noisy

The seasonal movement of animals from one region to another.
(a) migraet
(b) migreat
(c) migrate

A person who installs and repairs pipes and fittings for water supply or drainage.
(a) plummer
(b) plumber
(c) plumer

Shy or easily frightened.
(a) timmid
(b) timid
(c) timmed

Requiring or involving a lot of effort and energy.
(a) strenous
(b) strenuous
(c) straneous

SCORE   /10

193

Assessment: Lessons 15-16

Select the correct word.

The action or power of focusing one's attention or mental effort.
(a) concentration
(b) consentration
(c) concentracian

The number below the line in a fraction.
(a) denominator
(b) denominater
(c) denomenator

Showing a heartfelt and powerful intensity.
(a) fearce
(b) fierse
(c) fierce

Plural of "half," meaning two equal parts of something.
(a) halvs
(b) halves
(c) halfs

An attorney.
(a) lawyer
(b) laywer
(c) lawiar

A person, plant, or animal that is descended from a particular ancestor.
(a) descendent
(b) descendant
(c) desendant

A mathematical rule or relationship expressed in symbols.
(a) formieula
(b) formula
(c) formeula

Deep sorrow, especially caused by someone's death.
(a) grief
(b) greif
(c) greef

Extremely funny or entertaining, causing laughter.
(a) hilairious
(b) hilerious
(c) hilarious

To seek information by asking a question.
(a) inqwire
(b) inquier
(c) inquire

SCORE /10

Assessment: Lessons 17-18

Select the correct word.

To move by jumping on one foot.
(a) hopp
(b) hop
(c) hope

To happen or take place.
(a) occurr
(b) occure
(c) occur

A group of sports teams or organizations that compete against each other.
(a) leegue
(b) leageu
(c) league

Something that is considered more important or takes precedence over others.
(a) priority
(b) priorety
(c) pryority

To care for and encourage the growth or development of someone or something.
(a) nurteure
(b) nurture
(c) nurtuer

A person who resists or opposes authority, control, or tradition.
(a) rebel
(b) rebal
(c) rebbel

Willing to obey or follow rules and instructions.
(a) obedient
(b) obediant
(c) obiedient

The action of repeating something that has already been said or written.
(a) repetision
(b) repetition
(c) repitition

Related to the body or physical activity; tangible.
(a) fizical
(b) fysical
(c) physical

A space that is empty of matter.
(a) vaccuum
(b) vacum
(c) vacuum

SCORE   /10

Assessment: Lessons 19-20

Select the correct word.

Emitting light or shining brightly.
(a) luminous
(b) lumminous
(c) luminus

Extremely fierce or aggressive.
(a) ferocius
(b) ferocious
(c) feroshious

To bring something up or speak about it, usually briefly.
(a) menshion
(b) mention
(c) mansion

Having a strong or eager interest or enthusiasm.
(a) kean
(b) keene
(c) keen

A tissue that is a part of the body's system for movement.
(a) mussel
(b) mucsle
(c) muscle

A special skill or talent for doing something easily.
(a) Gnak
(b) knack
(c) nack

The number above the line in a fraction.
(a) numeraetor
(b) numerator
(c) newmerater

Attractively old-fashioned in a charming and picturesque way.
(a) quaint
(b) qwaint
(c) queaint

A long and often adventurous journey in search of something.
(a) quest
(b) qwest
(c) queste

The desire to do something, especially something wrong or unwise.
(a) temptation
(ab temptashun
(c) temptaetion

SCORE   /10

Synonym Puzzles
Solutions
and
Answer Key

1

2

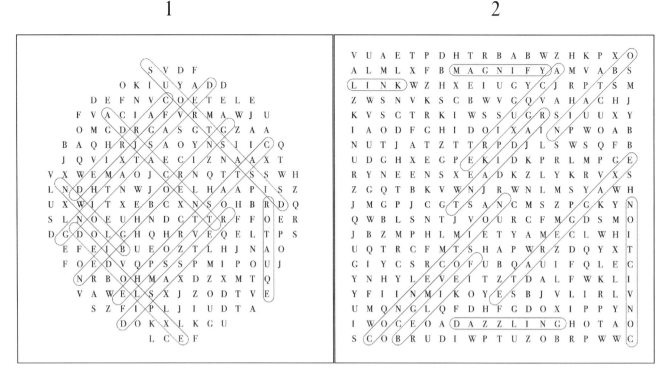

1

Synonyms

adjacent	⟶	neighbouring
blown	⟶	exploded
catastrophe	⟶	disaster
disastrous	⟶	devastating
equator	⟶	no synonym

2

Synonyms

acquire	⟶	obtain
belief	⟶	conviction
connection	⟶	link
dazzling	⟶	radiant
exaggerate	⟶	magnify

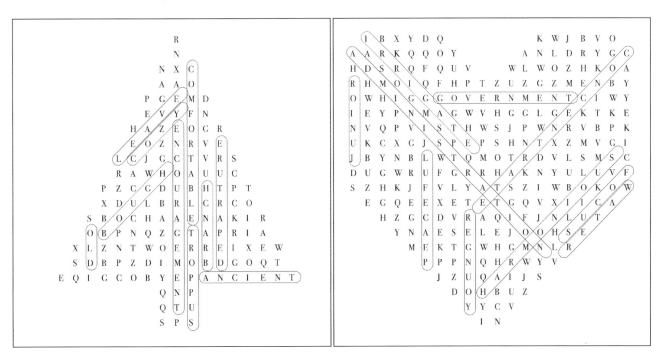

3
Synonyms

ancient	⟶	old
bough	⟶	branch
comfortable	⟶	cozy
departure	⟶	leave
encouragement	⟶	support

4
Synonyms

focus	⟶	concentrate
government	⟶	administration
harmonious	⟶	peaceful
irrigate	⟶	water
junior	⟶	younger

5

6

5
Synonyms

fragile	——————▶	delicate
gaze	——————▶	stare
involve	——————▶	include
jovial	——————▶	cheerful
knowledge	——————▶	expertise

6
Synonyms

labyrinth	——————▶	maze
metaphor	——————▶	analogy
narrate	——————▶	recount
origin	——————▶	beginning
peculiar	——————▶	unusual

7

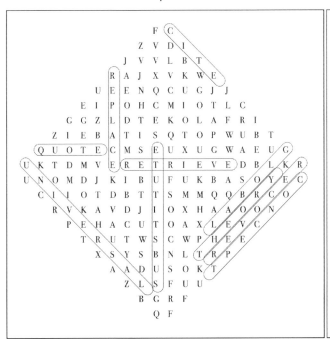

8

7
Synonyms

quote	——→	cite
retrieve	——→	recover
substitute	——→	replace
theory	——→	concept
universal	——→	global

8
Synonyms

reinforce	——→	strengthen
source	——→	origin
tangible	——→	material
unique	——→	distinct
vivid	——→	bright

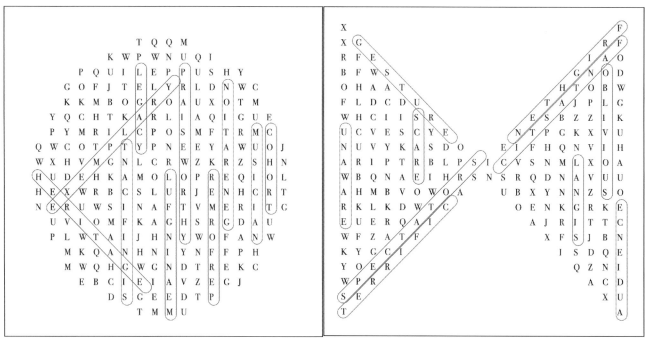

9
Synonyms

exemplary	⟶	praiseworthy
generation	⟶	cohort
legacy	⟶	heritage
musician	⟶	performer
significant	⟶	meaningful

10
Synonyms

audience	⟶	spectators
frighten	⟶	scare
gesture	⟶	signal
oblivious	⟶	unaware
terrific	⟶	fantastic

11

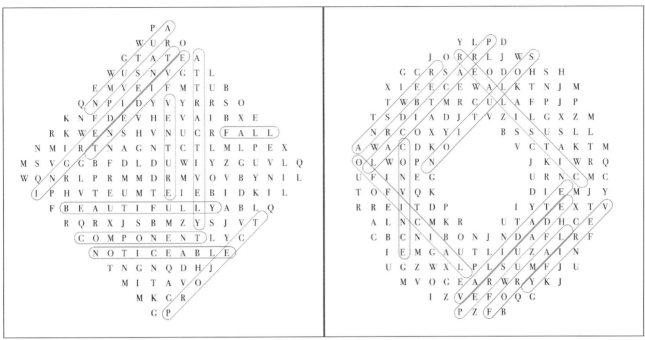

11
Synonyms

autumn	→	fall
beautifully	→	attractively
noticeable	→	evident
ingredient	→	component
venture	→	project

12
Synonyms

official	→	formal
persuade	→	convince
realistic	→	practical
solution	→	answer
verify	→	validate

13

14

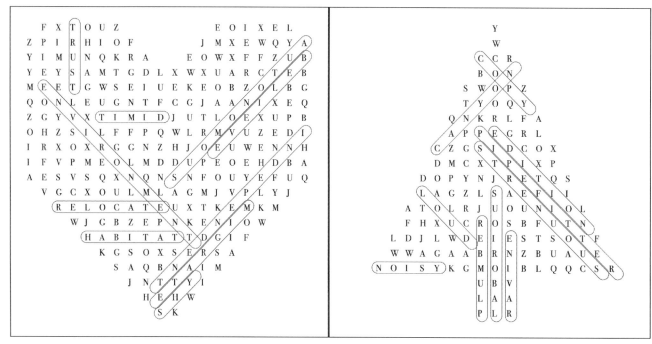

13
Synonyms

believe	⟶	trust
habitat	⟶	environment
independent	⟶	autonomous
migrate	⟶	relocate
timid	⟶	shy

14
Synonyms

canyon	⟶	ravine
edition	⟶	copy
noisy	⟶	loud
plumber	⟶	pipefitter
strenuous	⟶	laborious

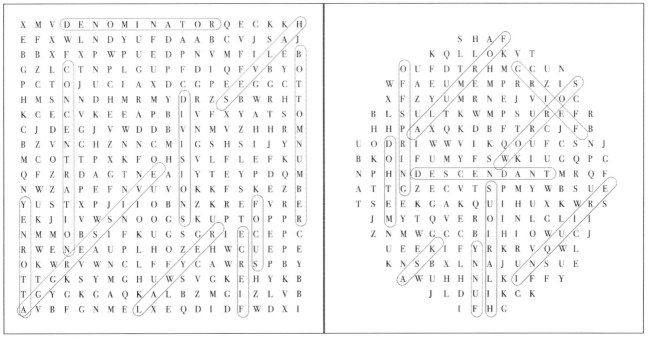

15
Synonyms

concentration	→	focus
denominator	→	bottom number
fierce	→	aggressive
halves	→	divisions
lawyer	→	attorney

16
Synonyms

descendant	→	offspring
formula	→	method
grief	→	sorrow
hilarious	→	funny
inquire	→	ask

17

18

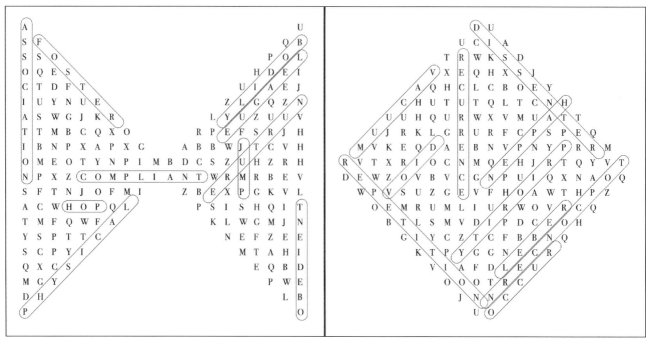

17
Synonyms

hop	⟶	jump
league	⟶	association
nurture	⟶	foster
obedient	⟶	compliant
physical	⟶	bodily

18
Synonyms

occur	⟶	happen
priority	⟶	top concern
rebel	⟶	dissenter
repetition	⟶	recurrence
vacuum	⟶	void

19

19
Synonyms

luminous	→	bright
mention	→	bring up
muscle	→	tissue
numerator	→	top number
quest	→	expedition

20

20
Synonyms

ferocious	→	savage
keen	→	interested
knack	→	talent
quaint	→	old-fashioned
temptation	→	lure

Further Studies for 7th Grade

Vocabulary Building 7th Grade

- Definitions
- Model Sentences
- Fill-in-the-blank
- Answer Key

Vocabulary and Spelling 7th Grade

- Definitions
- Model Sentences
- Varied Vocabulary Activities
- Spelling Activities
- Answer Key
- Tests
- Test Scoring Tables
- Recommendations

The Spelling Practice Workbook 7th Grade

- Definitions
- Model Sentences
- Spelling Activities
- Synonyms Word Search
- Answer Key

Available on Amazon

Scan code with your phone.

Made in United States
Orlando, FL
26 March 2024